THE
MODEL ENGINEER'S
LATHE MANUAL

WE'VE NEVER SEEN THE POINT OF HIDING OUR EXTRAS

With every screw cutting centre lathe or vertical milling machine we sell, you'll get a little something extra.

It's called a Tooling and Ancillary Equipment Catalogue.

When you've been manufacturing high quality precision machine tools as long as we have (over 60 years), you come to know a good deal about the importance of machine versatility.

That's why we also manufacture an enormous range of extra machine equipment. Everything from angle plates and boring bars through to tee bolts and vee blocks.

Your catalogue is just part of the after-sales service on offer from Myford. To find out more Telephone (0115) 9254222 or write to the Sales Dept., Myford Ltd., Chilwell Road, Beeston, Nottingham NG9 1ER, England.

Myford

QUALITY – TO BE PRECISE!

THE
MODEL ENGINEER'S
LATHE MANUAL

by
EDGAR T. WESTBURY

TEE Publishing
Warwickshire, England

To the craftsmen of the world, whose skill of brain
and hand creates the unlimited variety of useful and
beautiful products essential to civilisation.

First published as *Metal Turning Lathes* 1970

Reprinted 1995

© TEE Publishing ISBN 1 85761 098 9

Printed and bound in Great Britain at
Redwood Books, Trowbridge, Wiltshire

PREFACE

MANY books have been written about the lathe, from various aspects, including its history, development, and its application to the requirements of amateur and professional users. Special types of lathes, with many attachments, for ornamental work, and others designed for the most efficient industrial production, have all had their quota of literature devoted to them. Most of them have contributed to practical knowledge within their own sphere. My book, *The M.E. Lathe Manual*, although primarily devoted to the use of the lathe for model engineering, contained a good deal of information on the wider use of the lathe for general purposes.

The general principles of lathe design, and their mode of operation, have not changed in many years, but there have been many detail improvements in both respects over the years. In particular, standards of accuracy in machine tools, and in the work they are expected to produce, have risen considerably. Efficiency in the operation of lathes has increased, largely due to the availability of better tool steels, but this in turn has made it necessary to improve structure and mechanical design of lathes, and apply more power to driving them.

Accessory equipment has followed similar trends in robustness and accuracy, and chucks of all kinds are better than ever before. Aids to accuracy, such as feed screw indices, measuring and testing equipment, have also improved. But in the end, the quality and accuracy of work produced in the lathe depends on the proper use of cutting tools, and these have been dealt with in fairly minute detail, but without dogma. There are always several ways of doing the same job, and craftsmen all have their individual ideas on how to sharpen and set tools; the most essential thing is to understand the principles on which the tools operate.

A more comprehensive range of sizes of lathes is dealt with than in former books, and embraces all those used in general engineering, from the smallest sizes to about 6 in. centre height, but excluding small watchmaking lathes on one hand, and heavy industrial lathes at the other extreme. Small and relatively simple lathes, once regarded as suitable only for amateurs, are rapidly finding a useful place in light industry, and particularly development laboratories for instrumentation and electronics. At the same time, many amateurs are turning to larger lathes, for building model locomotives of 5 in. gauge or over, and similar large-scale projects. It has not been possible to describe all contemporary lathes in detail, due to space limitations, but those dealt with embody typical features of design, and I have had practical experience with their use.

In the course of many years as a technical writer, I have been asked innumerable questions on matters appertaining to problems in lathe work, and I have endeavoured to answer as many of these as possible within the compass of this book. No apology is made for the elementary nature of some of the explanations, because it has been found that not only beginners, but also some more advanced turners, can profit by practical hints on difficult or unusual aspects of lathe work. It is often said that skilled crafts cannot be taught by books, and it is perfectly true that proficiency can only be achieved by constant practice, but a practical book can help the reader to grasp essential principles, and avoid errors which might otherwise be perpetuated through lack of sound guidance.

One of the great difficulties in technical writing lies in the inadequacy, also ambiguity, of available terminology. Some of the terms used in engineering appear to have been invented on the spur of the moment, or adapted from familiar and non-technical objects. As a result, it is not easy to define clearly and accurately some of the important components, or even processes, involved in lathe work. For instance, the word "centre", may mean an abstract geometrical point, a conical accessory with a taper shank, or an indentation in the end of a shaft produced by centre-drilling. This often makes it necessary to use several works for a definite explanation where one, or a very few, should suffice, and the writer may be accused of using kindergarten language instead of proper technical terms.

In view of the possibility that within a few years, the measurements now used in British engineering practice may become obsolete, some attention has been given to the problems involve in such matters as working to metric dimensions or cutting metric threads. But there are no insuperable problems in changing over to different standards, neither does it call for drastic changes in the design of equipment, or methods of operation, of lathes. In some branches of engineering, metric standards of measurement have been in use for several years, and operators have managed well enough with the aid of simple conversion tables and reasonable intelligence. Therefore it is not considered that the lathes described in this book will be rendered obsolete by any changes in units of measurement.

EDGAR T. WESTBURY

PUBLISHER'S NOTE

The author's first major book on lathes and lathe work was *The M.E. Lathe Manual* published in 1951. This was subsequently revised and much of the contents incorporated in the present book which was published under the title *Metal Turning Lathes*. In reprinting the work, we have decided to revert to the original title, *The Model Engineer's Lathe Manual*, since this more accurately reflects the use today of the size and type of the machinery described herein.

CONTENTS

LIST OF ILLUSTRATIONS

CHAPTER 1

THE EVOLUTION OF THE LATHE

THE various metal-working crafts employed in engineering entail the need for many kinds of tools and appliances, some of which are operated entirely by hand, while others are driven, and to some extent manipulated, by mechanical means. These are generally classified as "machine tools", and the most important of them all is the lathe, which is essential in the production of nearly every form of component for engines and machines. The term "lathe" has been applied to a wide variety of appliances, from the severely simple to the elaborate and complex, and includes grinding, lapping and polishing machines, lapidaries' wheels for cutting precious stones, drilling and boring tools, and some in which hand or mechanically-controlled cutting tools are employed. A common feature of all these machines is the use of a rotating spindle by which the power is applied either to the operating tool or the work itself. The class of lathe to be dealt with in this book is that designed particularly for working with metal (though adaptable to other materials) and within a range of size and capacity capable of being driven by manual power, or fractional-horse-power motors.

Before discussing the essential features of these lathes, the various ways in which materials can be shaped or formed may be briefly discussed. These include ductile *deformation*, such as by forging, rolling, extrusion, and die-pressing; *shearing*, as in guillotines, blanking, punching and nibbling machines; and by *cutting*, with tools which slice, pare or chip away the surplus material. In all these processes, machine tools can be used to advantage. The production of parts by *casting* molten metal in sand or metal dies does not normally entail the use of machine tools as generally understood, though certain specialised machines are used in industry to speed up and improve accuracy of foundry processes. *Fusion* processes, such as welding and flame cutting, are in a similar category, though some of the appliances for these purposes which are now coming into industrial use conform practically to the definition of machine tools.

These processes are briefly mentioned in order to present a clear picture of all the possible methods of working metal, so that the most practicable, economical and efficient method for carrying it out with available facilities can be selected. The lathe, although specifically intended for use with cutting tools, can also be employed in deformation processes such as spinning, winding of springs or coils, rolling or swaging, and shearing or incision. Machines comparable to lathes are employed in foundries, for centrifugal casting

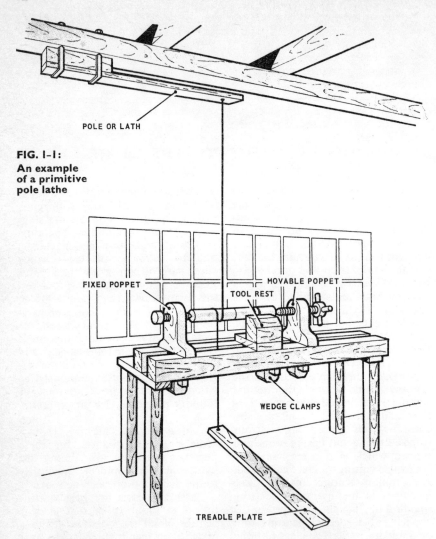

POLE OR LATH

FIG. I–I:
An example
of a primitive
pole lathe

FIXED POPPET

MOVABLE POPPET

TOOL REST

WEDGE CLAMPS

TREADLE PLATE

of tubes and hollow cylinders. There
are, in fact, few mechanical processes
to which lathes cannot be applied or
adapted.

Industrial craftsmanship, from the
very earliest times, has made good
use of various kinds of lathes,
though mostly of crude types, until
the advent of engines and machinery
at the latter end of the eighteenth
century, which gave a great incentive
to their improvement and called for
greater efficiency and capacity for
work. The evolution of the lathe
from its primitive beginnings may be
compared to that of machines for
the manufacture of textile products.
This began with the distaff, which
was hand-powered, and called for
considerable manipulative skill; it
was the direct progenitor of the
spinning wheel and hand loom,

which improved production efficiency and also the quality of the product. But whereas these appliances have been superseded completely by complex automatic machinery (except in a very few special cases) the modern general-purpose lathe is still an important essential in all engineering crafts, capable of productive and creative work.

Lathes of primitive type, some of which survive up to the present day, consist of little more than a horizontal bed on which are mounted two pedestals or "poppets", one or both of which can be adjusted along the bed to cope with work of varying length. Pointed rods or "dead centres" are fitted in the poppets, to line up with each other, and these form the only bearings; the workpiece, which is indented or "centre-drilled" at both ends, is mounted between them, and rotated by means of a cord wound round it at any convenient position. To support the cutting tool, a hand rest of some kind is provided, and this may be adjustable both lengthwise and crosswise relative to the work. The cord may be stretched across a bow of whalebone or other elastic material, or suspended from an overhead lath or "pole", which serves the purpose of returning the cord to its original position after it has been pressed down by a foot stirrup or treadle plate to rotate the work. Pole lathes have been used by wood turners, and particularly by chairmakers, up to quite recent times; and a form of dead-centre appliance, commonly known as "turns", is still used, in conjunction with a bow, by some watchmakers.

The principle of mounting work between dead centres, and rotating it against the action of the cutting tool, as in Fig. 1–3A, is basically sound; it is a true generating process, in which the truth or alignment of the point centres do not affect the circular accuracy of the finished work. But it has obvious disadvantages, which limit efficiency of production. It is not convenient to rotate the work by a cord in the ways described, as the motion is intermittent, and the power available is limited. In a modified arrangement of the dead centre principle, which is extensively employed in special forms of modern lathes, also in cylindrical

FIG. 1–2: Watchmakers' dead centre lathe, or "turns"

14   METAL-TURNING LATHES

grinding machines, the dead centres are retained, but the work is driven by means of a driver pulley, which is mounted to run freely on an extension of one of the poppets. Motion is transmitted through a driver pin in the pulley and a carrier clamped to the work. This enables the work to be driven continuously, and its power and speed are limited only by the size of the pulley and the belt or other form of drive applied. Fig. 1–3B

The next important development in lathe design was the introduction of the "live mandrel", which consisted of a shaft fitted to bearings in one of the poppets, and carrying one or more driving pulleys, besides a live centre, and means of transmitting motion to the work. This comprised a driver or "catchplate", or a disc "faceplate" to which the work could be bolted directly, without the need for support between two centres. Not only could power be

more efficiently applied in this way, but variation of speed could also be obtained by the use of stepped pulleys; in the event of high torque at low speed being required, the mandrel could be driven through reduction gearing at any suitable ratio. Fig. 1–3C

The driving end poppet came to be known as the live "headstock" in lathes of this type, and the other was termed the "tailstock" or "loose headstock". While the practical benefits of the live mandrel were beyond dispute, the quality of the work produced by its aid was largely dependent on the accuracy and adjustment of its bearings. Any error in roundness or concentric running of the mandrel was liable to be transmitted to the finished work, and this applied also to any error in concentricity of the live centre. But it was the first step towards transforming the lathe from a crude appliance to a real machine tool. Among many others who contributed to the early development of the lathe, the versatile genius Leonardo da Vinci recorded in his notebooks sketches of lathes, showing improved details of design and methods of driving them.

Some lathes of quite early period had some means of guiding or controlling the motion of the cutting tool, with a view to improving the accuracy of the work produced, and making it less dependent on the skill of the operator. But with the imperfect constructional methods available at the time, such devices were not very satisfactory. The first practical development in this direction is credited to Henry Maudslay, who built lathes in the early nineteenth century which had many

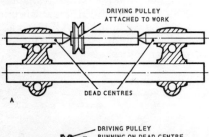

DRIVING PULLEY ATTACHED TO WORK

DEAD CENTRES

A

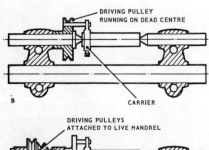

DRIVING PULLEY RUNNING ON DEAD CENTRE

B

CARRIER

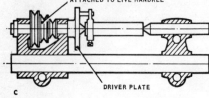

DRIVING PULLEYS ATTACHED TO LIVE MANDREL

DRIVER PLATE

C

FIG. 1–3: The evolution of the simple lathe

important improvements both in design and construction. The bed of the Maudslay lathe was made from one or more straight triangular bars, laid horizontally with the apex upwards. It was possible to make this straight and true by simple methods, and to check its accuracy when made, together with the angular seatings of the fast and loose head-stocks fitted to it, thus preserving true alignment of the centres at any position on the bed. A sliding saddle or "carriage" was also fitted to the bed, capable of being moved along it by a feed screw or other means, and having a tool holder with radial adjustment for the cutting tool. The "slide rest" as it was called, enabled truly cylindrical and parallel work to be produced without difficulty; in some form or other it is an essential feature of all modern metal turning lathes. Fig. 1–4

At this period, it was difficult to produce accurate threads, and most of the machines then made bore evidence of this by evading the use of screws in their construction. From clocks and watches to heavy steam engines, cotters and wedges were often used to hold parts together.

FIG. 1–4: Maudslay's original screw-cutting lathe circa 1800 (South Kensington Science Museum)

The possibility of producing threads and helices in the lathe by controlled endwise movement of the tool, in relation to the rotation of the work, had long been recognised, but had hitherto been very imperfectly carried out. Maudslay introduced the master or "lead" screw, which could be geared to the live mandrel at any required ratio by spur gears having varied numbers of teeth. This was used to propel the carriage on which a pointed cutting tool was mounted, so that it would cut a helix having a "lead" or pitch dependent on the rotational speed of the lead screw in relation to that of the live mandrel. This principle has been employed in all general-purpose engineering lathes for cutting threads ever since.

But bearing in mind that in Maudslay's time no really accurate screws existed, the problem of how to produce a satisfactory master screw arose. This was solved by mounting a cylinder of soft metal in the lathe, and presenting an incising tool (like a broad chisel) tangentially to it at an angle calculated to produce a helix of the required pitch. The carriage was free to slide with the minimum friction, and the tool adjusted radially to dig into the surface of the cylinder, the rotation of which caused the tool to move along its length. This produced a rudimentary but accurate helix, which in turn could be used to generate threads in steel or other metals.

During the nineteenth century many practical improvements were made in lathes for engineering work by Sir Joseph Whitworth and other inventors. These were mainly concerned with making the lathes capable of carrying out heavier work, increasing their range of utility, and durability under working conditions. The Whitworth type of lathe set the pattern for sound, accurate lathes, which was followed in Britain and abroad for many years, and is still in evidence in modified form.

In the same period, lathes of a very different type were developed for the primary purpose of ornamental turning, which was then a very popular hobby with devotees in all classes, including the nobility, and even royalty, in several countries. The most noted designers of these lathes were Holtzapffel and Evans, who produced very elaborate machines with various types of mandrels, slide rests, and attachments for indexing, flycutting and geometric movements, calling for innumerable cutting tools and other accessories. Some lathes were also made with rocking headstocks for "rosette" or other non-circular pattern turning, and traversing mandrels for cutting threads of limited pitch, in conjunction with followers with segmental internal threads. In most cases, the complications in these lathes were of very little use in general engineering, where it was

more profitable to develop special machines for operations other than straightforward turning. At least one serious attempt to embody the facilities of the ornamental turning lathe in an accurate and robust metal-turning lathe was made by Pittler towards the end of the nineteenth century. But to all intents and purposes, ornamental turning lathes are now extinct, though some of their features, particularly in respect of attachments, are still found very useful in small lathes which have to be adapted to the widest possible range of operations, in the absence of other machines.

A large proportion of small lathes for both amateur and professional use are equipped for screwcutting, as this is essential to many kinds of engineering work, and can be carried out in the lathe more accurately than by taps and dies in most cases, apart from having a much wider range of application. Such lathes are fitted with a lead screw which can be gear-driven from the live mandrel, using change wheels of various sizes and numbers of teeth to produce the most useful standard pitches. For convenience in operation, some means of disconnecting the lead screw drive is generally fitted, such as a dog clutch, or a split nut in the saddle, which can be opened to release the lead screw by means of a cam and hand lever. To avoid the tedious operation of setting up trains of change wheels for every different pitch, many lathes have a change-speed gearbox, either built in as a standard component, or available as an extra, by means of which the ratio of the lead screw can be varied by shifting one or more levers. The Norton type of gearbox, on which most modern examples are based, essentially contains a row of different-sized spur change gears on a single shaft, and a sliding tumbler gear which can be meshed with any one of the change gears to transmit its motion either directly or indirectly to the lead screw.

Apart from the use of the geared lead screw for cutting threads, it is even more extensively employed to provide an automatic traverse, better known as "self-act", to the saddle. This is not only an advantage in avoiding the need for manual work when taking long traversing cuts, but it will generally produce a better finish by moving the saddle more continuously and uniformly, at a rate regulated by the ratio of the lead screw drive. Fine feeds are obtained by gearing of specially high reduction ratio, obtained either by setting up change wheels, or through the gearbox. The more elaborate types of lathes often have a separate drive shaft for the self-acting traverse, independent of the lead screw and its gear train. Radial movement of the cross slide can also be driven automatically by another special form of gearing. To provide a means of reversing the rotation of the lead screw in relation to the mandrel, simple screwcutting lathes have provision for introducing an extra gear into the driving gear train, but in modern lathes, this is more often carried out by means of a gear cluster or "tumbler", with a lever giving forward, reverse and neutral positions.

CHAPTER 2

MODERN METAL-TURNING LATHES

THE lathes described in this chapter are nearly all of British design, and most are in current production at the time of writing. They cover a range of sizes in the general-pupose category, or as they are commonly called "centre lathes", though the latter term also may quite correctly be applied to certain types of special-purpose lathes which have provision for mounting work between point or hollow centres. The size of British lathes is usually specified in terms of centre height, in conjunction with the maximum length of work which can be admitted between centres. In America, it is more common to specify the diametral capacity, or "swing" of the lathe, so that a lathe of 4-in. centres would be defined as an 8-in. lathe by this standard. All the lathes have certain basic features in common, but vary widely in detail design, according to the class of work for which they are primarily intended.

Apart from the matter of size, a paramount consideration in the selection of a lathe is that it should be well suited to the kind of work most likely to be encountered. No lathe is capable of dealing efficiently with every kind of work, and the definition "general purpose" can only be applicable within certain limits. There has been a great deal of speculation and discussion on the type of machine which would suit

everybody, but it has not yet materialised, and the so-called "ideal" lathe is in practice a romantic myth.

But the general-purpose lathe should be capable of a very wide range of turning operations, and in cases where the workshop equipment is limited, it is often called upon to serve as a kind of universal machine to deal with many kinds of work besides turning as generally understood. The versatility of the lathe is therefore a valuable asset, but generally speaking, attempts to make it equally suitable for every kind of machining operation have not been highly successful. They usually result either in a highly elaborate and complicated machine which is too expensive to be acceptable to most of the users for which it is intended, or a gadget machine which will do everything after a fashion, but nothing really well—in fact a "Jack of all trades but master of none".

Accuracy is a feature much to be desired in any machine tool, and the reputation of a lathe may stand or fall by its virtues in this respect. In recent years, standards of accuracy for machine tools, including the well-known Schlesinger limits, have been set up to define the essential factors of concentricity, alignment, etc., which are considered desirable in machines. Generally speaking, however, these can only be observed in high class industrial machine tools; the types of lathes which have to be built at a competitive price are often sold without any guarantee in respect of accuracy. Though a certain class of lathe may be described as a "precision" lathe, this term is very vague, and does not necessarily mean that it conforms to any definite standard of accuracy. True precision is a very expensive commodity, as it entails not only making the lathe to very fine limits in every structural and working part, but also meticulous testing of the complete lathe assembly when finished.

In the past, many small lathes have been manufactured in which accuracy was very dubious, but in view of their low cost, their imperfections were tolerated, and they served the purpose for which they were intended quite well. It does not follow that accurate work is only possible if the machine tool itself is above reproach; but it will obviously take longer, and require more skill, than where the machine has built-in accuracy. For this reason, the professional worker, who must carry out accurate work in minimum time, in order to earn a living, will need a highly accurate and efficient lathe; but the requirements of the amateur, to whom time is of less importance, may be adequately served by a simpler and less expensive lathe.

Most of the faults and imperfections of inexpensive lathes are capable of correction by adjustment of their working parts. Sometimes more radical treatment, such as refitting of slides and bearings, may be necessary to improve the accuracy of a cheaply constructed lathe. In many cases, such lathes, in the hands of intelligent users, have been converted to precision lathes, in the true sense of the term, by these methods. Although bad design, in respect of basic mechanical principles, is beyond

remedy and cannot be defended, simple and rugged construction is often a practical virtue. In the hands of an inexperienced operator, the basic principles of turning are readily grasped on a lathe having few and simple movements or controls; while a careless or inconsiderate operator may be a very expensive risk if turned loose on an elaborate and complex lathe.

The lathes used by watchmakers are of a specialised type, which do not come properly within the scope of this book. Not only their design, but also their mode of operation, differ from that of lathes employed in general engineering, apart from the matter of size and capacity. They may be described as the logical evolution of the dead-centre "turns" formerly employed for horological work, though they are now fitted with live mandrels, and often with compound slide rests as well. Larger lathes, intended specially for instrument makers, are designed on similar lines. For specific information on this class of lathes, the handbook *The Watchmaker's Lathe and how to use it* by Donald de Carle (N.A.G. Press) is recommended.

The smallest lathes designed for general engineering application are of $1\frac{5}{8}$ in. centre height and admit a length of 6 in. between centres. A pioneer of this type was the Adept, introduced in the 1930s by F. W. Portass Ltd. of Sheffield. It was at first regarded as little more than a toy, but it has proved capable of a wide range of useful work in miniature model engineering, and has also been adapted to horology, including gear wheel and pinion cutting, with the aid of suitable attachments. A lathe of similar dimensions and basic design, but improved in detail, and built to modern standards of accuracy, was that known as the Centrix "Micro" lathe. The machines in this

FIG. 2–1: Centric Micro 1⅝ in. lathe

class have all the salient features of larger engineering lathes, including a sliding saddle with traverse over the effective length of the bed, fully compound slide rest with boring table and swivelling top slide, barrel tailstock, with or without set-over adjustment, and socketed mandrel and tailstock barrel to take taper centres. The Centrix lathe had a three-step cone pulley for V-belt drive, and was equipped with a countershaft in a swinging bracket which provided for shifting and tensioning the belt. Fig. 2–1.

A larger but basically similar lathe was made by Flexispeed Machine Tools Ltd., known as the Meteor II, redesigned and improved version of a machine which was introduced over twenty years ago. It had a centre height of 2 in., and admits 24 in. between centres, thus providing sufficient capacity for a wide range of model work. In addition to the three speed ratios provided by the cone pulley, back gear giving a reduction of 4 to 1 was fitted. This enabled the lathe to cope with castings and other

relatively large pieces which call for slow speed and heavy torque. A special feature of this lathe was the self-acting feed, comprising a double reduction worm gear which could be brought into engagement with the lead screw to traverse the saddle at the rate of 0·0015 in. per revolution of the mandrel. The lead screw was of 8 t.p.i. and it was therefore possible to adapt the lathe for screw-cutting, by the addition of change wheels of various size to cover the required range of thread pitches. A four-way turret tool post was fitted, and the headstock pulleys and gearing were provided with metal guards. Fig. 2–2.

The Unimat 9 (originally the Emco-Unimat, of Continental origin) is distributed in Britain by Elliott Machine Equipment Ltd, Bec House, Victoria Road, NW10 6NY. It is described as a universal machine tool, being applicable to many kinds of operations besides lathe work. Its design is unique, and includes a self-contained headstock unit with motor and countershaft, which is normally mounted directly on the main bedplate, but can also be mounted on a vertical pillar, with the mandrel vertical or at any required angle. The saddle and tailstock, also the cross slide, are fitted on slide bars—a feature, it may be mentioned, which has often been employed in the past on small lathes—and screw feeds are provided for both longitudinal and cross slide movements. An open-side tool post is mounted on the cross slide, which has a single T-slot to take the holding down-bolt. No swivelling slide is fitted, but taper turning can be carried out by swivelling the complete headstock unit on the bed.

The mandrel assembly, with its bearings, is fitted in a cylindrical housing or "quill", which can be moved endwise by rack and pinion, or clamped in position. It is fitted with a three-step cone pulley for V-belt, and the driving motor and countershaft are mounted on a bracket, attached to the quill by means of a split clamp. Nine speeds, from 364 to 6,000 r.p.m., are obtainable with the standard countershaft arrangement. The motor fitted is of the universal (a.c./d.c.) type, rated at 90 watts, and fitted with interference suppressor. The centre height of the machine is 36 mm. (1·42 in.) equivalent to a swing of 70 mm. (2¾ in.), and maximum length

admitted between centres is 175 mm. (7 in.); bore through spindle is 6·5 mm. (¼ in.) and the mandrel traversing movement is 20 mm. (¾ in.) Fig. 2–3.

A wide range of attachments can be obtained for the Unimat, including a saw table, milling slide, fretsaw, extension bed, self acting feed, collet sleeve with draw-in screw for 8-mm. collets, extra slow speed countershaft, and hobbing appliance for cutting threads. These are in addition to the standard items of equipment such as chucks, centres and cutting tools.

Few machine tools have attained greater popularity in small workshops than those produced by Myford's Ltd., of Beeston, Nottingham. Since this firm was first established over thirty years ago, they have set out to produce lathes of sound design at the most competitive prices. During the war, they manufactured many special types of machine tools for the production of armaments, and also took over the production of the Drummond M

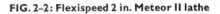

FIG. 2–2: Flexispeed 2 in. Meteor II lathe

FIG. 2–3: The Unimat 9 Universal Machine tool

type 3½-in. lathes, which at that time were regarded as the most advanced machines in their class. In post-war years, their principal products are the ML 7, ML 10 and Super-7 3½-in. lathes, which are very similar in capacity and basic design, but differ in detail, with several improvements and refinements in the latter type.

The ML 7 lathe will swing 7 in. diameter over the bed, with 4⅛ in. over the cross slide and 10 in. in the gap. It admits 20 in. maximum length between centres, and a special long-bed version, admitting 32 in., is available. The mandrel is bored through ⅝ in. diameter and socketed to take No. 2 Morse taper centres. It runs in plain, fully split bearings of anti-friction white metal, with a ball race to take end thrust. A three-step cone pulley is fitted to the mandrel, and reduction gearing (usually termed "back gear" but in this case located underneath the mandrel) is provided, giving a range of six speeds from 35 to 640 r.p.m. or 47 to 840 r.p.m., depending on the ratio of the motor to countershaft primary drive. The countershaft bracket and motor mounting are permanent attachments to the lathe, and are provided with guards for the belts and gearing.

A long sliding saddle, fitted to the outer shears of the bed, is provided, having an apron which contains the clasp nut for the lead screw and the pinion and handwheel for rack feed. The cross slide is of ample width and area to form a substantial boring table, and is provided with T-slots for clamping work. On it is mounted the swivelling top slide, which has a base of large diameter with a graduated index, and is held down by two bolts. The tool post is of the open clamp plate type, which gives the maximum facility for holding any type of tool. A hollow barrel tailstock, bored and socketed to correspond with the mandrel, is fitted. Its base has a tongue which fits the inner shears of the bed, and is provided with set-over adjustment. A lever-operated cam is employed for clamping it in position on the bed, and the barrel can also be locked by means of a wedge bolt with hand lever. Indices are provided on cross and top slide feed screws, and an indexed handwheel can be fitted to the lead screw. Fig. 2–4

The Super-7 lathe has an improved form of mandrel bearing, with a long tapered bronze bush at the front end, and a double ball thrust bearing, with provision for endwise adjustment, at the rear. This enables the running clearance to be very finely controlled, and also provides the maximum bearing area to carry radial loads, in conjunction with thrust loads. The tailstock is of the self-ejecting type, and the barrel is operated by a three-start thread and a ball thrust bearing, which gives sensitive control for drilling and similar operations. A specially long cross slide is fitted, with an improved method of mounting the top slide which enables it to be swivelled over a greater angle, but does not impair the use of the cross slide as a boring

table. Fourteen mandrel speeds can be obtained, from 25 to 2,150 r.p.m. with standard driving equipment.

The screwcutting arrangements for both lathes, by the use of change wheels and a tumbler reverse gear, are similar, but as an alternative, a quick-change gearbox can be fitted to simplify the selection of either screw pitches or self-acting feeds. The ML 7 can be fitted with the Tri-Leva driving unit which provides instant speed changes without the need for shifting the driving belt.

Boxford lathes are manufactured at Box Tree Mills, near Halifax, and have established a high reputation for sound design and accuracy in post-war years. Several types varying in details and equipment are produced, all of $4\frac{1}{2}$-in. centre height or 9-in. swing over the bed, but in different lengths to admit 16 in., 22 in., or 28 in. between centres. The general design follows American principles, including the bed, which

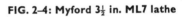

FIG. 2–4: Myford $3\frac{1}{2}$ in. ML7 lathe

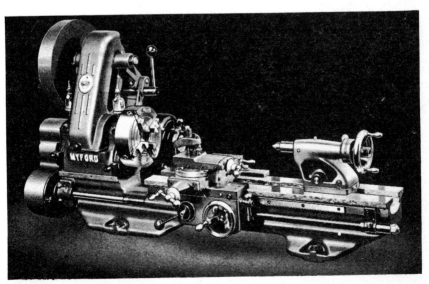

has inverted-V slideways and no gap. The headstock is of enclosed box section and the mandrel is fitted with opposed pre-loaded Timken roller bearings. Sixteen speeds from 30 to 1,300 r.p.m. are provided. A long saddle is fitted to the outer Vs of the bed, and both the cross and top slide feed screws have ball thrust bearings and graduated indices. The cross slide is not normally suited for use as a boring table, but a special table of large area, with T-slots, can be fitted. In addition to rack feed and clasp nut controls, the apron is equipped with gearing to provide self-acting cross feed. The tailstock slides on the inner V-ways of the bed, and has a self-ejecting feed screw to the barrel, also set-over adjustment to the base. Among special equipment and attachments a quick-change screwcutting gearbox, vertical milling slide, dividing head, and four-way turret may be fitted, and some models may be driven

through a variable speed gear which provides speeds from 50 to 2,000 r.p.m. Fig. 2–5.

The Viceroy lathes, introduced in recent years by Denford Small Tools Ltd., Brighouse, Yorks., are primarily intended for use in technical schools and training establishments, though they are equally well suited to general purposes. They are of 5 in. centre height, admitting 24 in. between centres, and have all-geared headstocks. The G.B. and T.D.S. models have separate feed shafts, in addition to the usual lead screw, for operating self-acting feeds. Models T.D.S. 4 and 5 B.G. are designed for primary training, and are not fitted with screwcutting gear or self-acting feeds. A special feature of the Viceroy lathes is the provision of safety devices which help to prevent damage to the machines or injury to the operators.

The Raglan Engineering Co. Ltd., Nottingham, established their reputation in post-war years with a 5 in. lathe known as the Little John, which had several distinctive features, including the use of hardened slide-

FIG. 2–5: Boxford 4½ in. lathe

FIG. 2–6: Colchester Bantam 5 in. lathe

ways attached to the bed, and variable speed drive. Some of these features are retained in the Raglan lathes in current production, which are classed as 5 in. lathes, though the actual centre height is $5\frac{1}{8}$ in. ($10\frac{1}{4}$ in. swing) and the length admitted between centres is 24 in. The stepless variable-speed gear is a permanent attachment, which employs expanding V-belt pulleys on motor and countershaft, and is controlled by a horizontal lever on top of the headstock casing, and incorporates a speed indicator. Mandrel speeds through the belt drive vary from 280 to 1,750 r.p.m., and through additional reduction (back) gear, from 38 to 260 r.p.m. The mandrel is of large diameter, bored $1\frac{9}{32}$ in. diameter and socketed to take No. 4 Morse centres. It runs in

Timken roller bearings in a rigid box section headstock casting, beneath which is located the quick-change screwcutting gearbox. Raglan machine tools also include the Loughborough 5 in. training lathe, of simple and robust design, without screwcutting gear, and a capstan lathe with gearless variable speed drive.

The Colchester Lathe Co., Colchester, Essex, is one of the oldest-established British machine tool manufacturing firms, and in pre-war days, their industrial lathes of small and medium size achieved a high reputation. At present their production is mainly concentrated on three types of lathes, of 5 or 6 in. centre

**FIG. 2–7:
Colchester
Student 6 in.
lathe**

height, admitting 20 in. between centres, namely the Bantam, the Student, and the Chipmaster. All have distinctive features of design; the first two have all-geared head-stocks, while the Chipmaster is driven through the Kopp variable-speed gear, giving a range of speeds from 35 to 3,000 r.p.m. Only the Student lathe has a gap bed, and this is provided with a gap piece which can be fitted to present a flush surface to the bed when required. All three lathes have mandrels running in Gamet taper roller bearings, with No. 3 Morse socket and flanged for Camlock chuck mounting; the slide ways of the bed have inverted V-guides, and are induction hardened.

The Student is specially suited for advanced training, while the Chip-master is more appropriate for toolroom use, being capable of

exceptionally high precision for a moderately priced machine. It can be fitted with a hydraulic-copying attachment, also a five-station cap-stan slide. Most of the accessories and attachments are applicable to Student and Bantam lathes as well, and include collet chucks, various forms of toolposts, and taper turning fixtures. Fig. 2–5, 6, 7.

Machine tools of several kinds have been manufactured by T. S. Harrison and Sons Ltd., of Heck-mondwike, Yorks., for many years. Their lathes in sizes within the scope of this book now include those of $4\frac{1}{2}$ in. and $5\frac{1}{2}$ in. centres (9 in. and 11 in. swing) both with straight bed or gap bed, to swing 17 in. and $18\frac{1}{4}$ in., with two lengths, admitting 24 in. or 40 in. between centres respectively. Apart from differences in dimensions, the specifications of these lathes are identical, including

**FIG. 2–8:
Colchester
Chipmaster
5 in. lathe**

all-geared headstocks giving a 16-speed range either from 34 to 1,500 or 45 to 1,000 r.p.m. The mandrel runs in Timken toller bearings at the front end, and a single-row ball bearing at the rear. It can be bored either 1⅜ in. with tapered socket for No. 3 Morse, or 1⅜ in. for American taper adaptor.

A 4 t.p.i. lead screw is fitted, and a separate shaft for driving longitudinal and cross self-acting feeds. As an alternative to the use of change wheels, a quick-change gearbox can be fitted. A wide range of accessories including vertical slide, dividing, taper turning, and toolpost grinding attachments, also a six-station indexing turret and cut-off slide. The larger sizes of Harrison lathes can be equipped with hydraulic copying attachments.

CHAPTER 3

ELEMENTS OF LATHE DESIGN

THE basic structural component of the lathe, which is also the largest and heaviest in most cases, is the bed, usually made in the form of an iron casting of channel or box girder section, having integral cross members or struts to provide the utmost rigidity. The top surface of the bed is machined to form a true seating for the headstock and tailstock, also a guide surface for the moving carriage or saddle. In most lathes the front and back of the top surface overhangs, and is machined parallel on the edges to maintain alignment of movable parts.

Many of the simpler types of lathes have the guide surfaces, or "shears", of dovetail section, with the underside guides of the saddle, and in some cases the tailstock as well, shaped to fit the angular surfaces. Other lathes have the sides of the bed machined square with the top surface, and the overhanging edges machined on the underside. Various other forms of lathe beds are employed, some of circular, part-circular, or prismatic cross section, also some in which one or more solid steel bars of round or square section are used as guides for the sliding parts. Bar bed lathes of small size have been popular in the past, but only one example is illustrated in this book; they have also been made in fairly large sizes for certain purposes. The triangular bar bed, as

used by Maudslay, though it survived for many years, is now obsolete, as it is difficult to make it rigid enough to suit modern conditions.

Modern practice favours a form of lathe bed in which the saddle and the tailstock are separately guided. One method of carrying this out is by providing a machined groove in the centre of the shears, and a close-fitting tongue on the underside of the tailstock, while the saddle fits over the full width of the shears, on the front part only. This principle has been developed in various ways, and some lathes have been built with completely separate slideways on the bed for the saddle and tailstock respectively. It is possible to arrange this so that the tailstock can be moved past the saddle if required.

Inverted V-form guides are employed on many of the larger and more expensive lathes, and have advantages in maintaining true alignment under working conditions, and reducing friction in the movement of sliding parts. Heavy slides will seat accurately by their own weight, and swarf tends to fall away from the contact surfaces rather than getting jammed under them. They are, however, more vulnerable to damage if heavy tools or workpieces are carelessly dropped on the lathe bed. The extra cost of machining slideways of this type is an objection to their use in small and relatively cheap lathes.

Most lathes have the full length of the bed machined to the same level, including the seating for the headstock. In a few cases, lathes have been made with the headstock cast integral with the bed; this has some constructional advantages, and helps to ensure rigidity of the complete assembly. But it calls for the utmost precision in the initial alignment of the headstock bearings with the slideways of the bed, because it is difficult to correct any errors in machining these parts, or which may be caused by subsequent distortion. Some lathes made with headstock and bed in one piece have the slideways attached in the form of strips, which can readily be machined all over and are capable of adjustment if this should be found necessary.

The provision of a gap in the bed immediately in front of the headstock enables work of relatively large diameter to be accommodated in lathes of limited centre height. It is sometimes objected to on the grounds that the gap weakens the bed and also deprives the saddle of adequate bearing surface at the place where it is most needed. But these disadvantages can be reduced or countered by good design. Some lathes are provided with a gap piece which can be fitted to a machined seating, to fill a part or the whole of the gap, and provide a flush bearing surface for the saddle. Most workpieces which call for a large swing are short in length and best suited to mounting on the faceplate. The only alternative to a gap bed lathe for such work is a lathe of sufficient centre height to give a clear swing over the bed, and this must necessarily be sturdier in all essential parts than one of smaller centre height, therefore more expensive to manufacture. Fig. 3–1.

Lathe beds are usually made in a hard but fine-grained cast iron which is initially machined by planing or sometimes by milling processes. After rough machining, the castings are usually "seasoned" to relieve stresses, and sometimes heat-treated to speed up this process. After final machining, lathe beds and other sliding surfaces were formerly finished to the highest possible precision by hand scraping, but this method is too slow for modern production, and has been superseded by slideway grinding in nearly all cases. Lathe beds can now be surface hardened by continuous processes, employing oxy-gas flames or electric induction heating, and quenching by water jets. This greatly increases their resistance to wear under heavy working conditions, but even without it, the durability of good cast iron is generally considered satisfactory for moderate duty over many years of service.

The means of supporting the bed on the underside, whether it is fitted to a stand or on a bench, must be so arranged that no stress is imposed which might cause distortion when it is bolted down. The cantilever type of bed, which has been employed in the past by Drummond's and other makers, had a single integral foot near the headstock end, which also helped to ensure rigidity in the region of the gap. This reduced risk of distortion, but it was only well suited to lathe beds of relatively short length, up to about 12 in. between centres. For extended length, an additional support under the tailstock was found desirable, but this defeated its original purpose. Most long bed lathes now have separate machined supporting castings under the extreme ends of the bed, and one or both of these may be combined with a pedestal stand, sometimes containing the driving gear or a quick-change gearbox.

Headstock and Bearings

An iron casting is generally employed also for the headstock, and again rigidity is a prime consideration; it is equally important that it should be bolted down securely or otherwise firmly attached to the bed. The bearings which carry the working spindle, or mandrel, as it is generally called, must be correctly aligned with the slideways of the bed, and well spaced to support the mandrel over a substantial length; this is less important for dealing with work mounted between centres than for chuck work which may overhang a considerable distance beyond the point of support. In such cases, the mandrel must serve as a rotating

cantilever beam, and both its length between bearings, and its diameter, must be substantial to obtain necessary rigidity.

Many different types of bearings have been used for lathes, and all have been satisfactory within their limitations, if accurately made and fitted. Early lathes for both wood and metal work were often fitted with a "cone-and-point" mandrel, in which the front part ran in a tapered bush, smallest at the nose end, and the back end was centre-drilled to run in contact with an adjustable point centre, which took the end thrust, and also enabled the radial clearance of the front bearing to be taken up. While sound in principle, this form of mandrel could not well be made hollow right through, and the size of the nose, with its register collar, was generally limited. Some

FIG. 3–1: Machining a component of large radius on a Harrison gap bed lathe

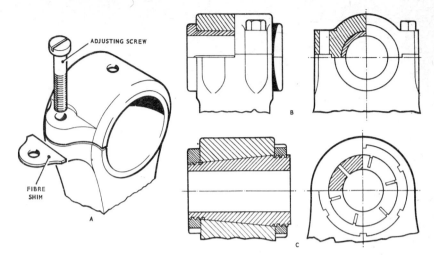

FIG. 3–2: Examples of plain bearings employed for lathe mandrels

lathes are still in use with mandrels of this or similar type, but it is obsolete in modern manufacture and need not be described here in greater detail.

Plain, parallel bearings are used on many small lathes and, fitted with equally simple mandrels, provide the cheapest form of assembly. They may be formed directly in the iron casting of the headstock, without bushings of any kind, and provided with a split lug and set screw, to allow a limited amount of adjustment for taking up wear. Provided that they are accurately bored and fitted, and run in with ample lubrication, the cast iron bearings will run with low frinction and last a long time. In order to retain oil in the bearings, resilient shims of appropriate thickness should be fitted in the gap, as shown in Fig. 3–2(a). Contrary to popular opinion, these bearings are not improved by fitting bronze bushes, as this is not the appropriate metal for use with an unhardened mandrel, and it is difficult to ensure that the bushes make positive contact with the bore of the housing all round when clamped by a single set

screw. If attempts are made to take up excessive slackness in these bearings, there is a risk of cracking them across the back, and it is not usually practicable to mend the headstock casting, by welding or other means, without causing inaccuracy through distortion.

Fully split bearings of the "plummer block" type, as shown in Fig. 3–2(b), are suitable for heavier duty, and can be fitted with split bushes, which can be initially bedded in and adjusted, also taken up and refitted after wear has taken place. In modern practice, thin pre-formed half-shells, lined with a thin layer of a suitable anti-friction white metal, can be used, and this gives long wear with either hardened or unhardened mandrel journals, if kept properly lubricated. The Myford ML 7 lathe has this type of bearing, but the Super 7 has a long tapered bronze bush at the front, and a pair of preloaded angular contact ball races at the back to take end thrust, and adjust running clearance of the front bush.

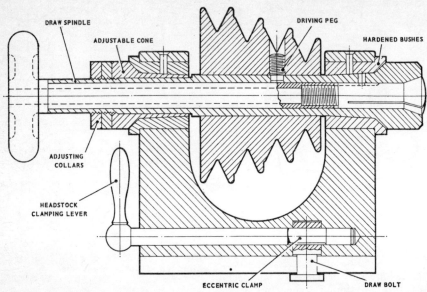

FIG. 3–3: Headstock of typical instrument lathe showing double opposed cone bearings

The contractable bush type of bearing has been used on several lathes in the past, including the $3\frac{1}{2}$ in. Drummond and Myford M type, but it is not in current production, so far as is known. It employs bushes in both front and rear housings, tapered on the outside, and split right through in one place, and partially through in several others. These are fitted to tapered bores in the headstock housings, and drawn in by ring nuts to compress the bushes inwards and thus adjust the running clearance on the mandrel, then locked by nuts on the large ends. This is an excellent form of bearing if accurately made and fitted, but it is relatively expensive, as it calls for special methods of boring the headstocks, and precise angular accuracy of the bushes. Fig. 3–2C.

A form of bearing which has been extensively used on small instrument lathes, and to a limited extent on larger machines, is the double-angular opposed cone type. It has often been described as the "ideal" lathe mandrel bearing, and it is based on the principle of coping with both radial and thrust loads in the most efficient manner. A mandrel having a journal with a parabolic contour, and a bearing to fit, was proposed for this purpose, but it was too difficult and expensive for general use. The compromise of a cone with two angles, one acute, for radial thrust, and the other obtuse for endwise thrust, was found more practicable. Lathes fitted with this bearing usually have parallel-bored headstocks with inserted bushes; the front cones are generally machined integral with the mandrel, and the rear cones are made a sliding fit for assembly and adjustment. They are keyed to prevent rotating on the mandrel, and after adjustment, are locked in position by ring nuts. The individual cones and their bushes must be machined to fit simultaneously on *both* angular surfaces. If they become worn, it is difficult to refit them, but they are usually made of hard and durable materials, so that this contingency does not arise. Fig. 3–3.

Plain bearing headstocks need to be fitted with means of taking up endwise play, and also for resisting end thrust such as that encountered in heavy drilling. Light lathes often have nothing more than a plain collar, sometimes with the addition of an anti-friction washer, to take the end thrust, and play is taken up by setting the drive pulley close to the back of the bearing. The use of a ball thrust race enables the friction under end load to be reduced, and means of fine adjustment for end play is a great advantage; especially for chuck and faceplate work. The thrust race may be fitted immediately behind the front collar of the mandrel, but this is open to the objection that it increases the overhang of the mandrel from its main bearing, and unless well enclosed, it is liable to collect dirt or metal dust. A better position is in front of the rear bearing, and this is general in good quality plain bearing lathes.

Ball journal bearings have been used in a few lathes, but have never been very popular. As the balls have a very limited area of working contact with the races, they lack the steadying effect of a well-fitted plain bearing with an oil film of large area, and are thus more liable to harshness and chattering. But it is not impossible to design a satisfactory ball bearing lathe headstock, preferably by using specially selected, pre-loaded angular-contact races, arranged back to back in a rigid housing or quill assembly.

The use of tapered roller bearings for lathe mandrels has generally been more successful, and they are now practically universal on the larger sizes of lathes. But much depends on the design of the complete bearing and headstock assembly, and the advantages of roller bearings for small, light lathes have often been questioned. Early attempts to fit them to headstocks with orthodox "pedestal" bearing housings were often unsuccessful, especially if the bearings were located

FIG. 3–4: A bearing suitable for lathes and other machine tools, employing Gamet taper roller bearings

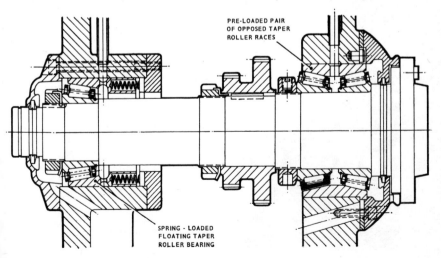

PRE-LOADED PAIR
OF OPPOSED TAPER
ROLLER RACES

SPRING - LOADED
FLOATING TAPER
ROLLER BEARING

at opposite ends of the lathe mandrel with a substantial distance between them. This is generally suited only to solid quill type housings with drive pulleys or gearing overhung at the tail end; but it is always open to the objection that any heat generated in the working of the machine causes an increase in the length of the mandrel, which may be sufficient to affect the adjustment of the roller bearings.

A bearing assembly suitable for lathes and other machine tools, employing precision taper roller races specially made for the purpose by Gamet Products Ltd., Colchester, Essex, is shown in Fig. 3–4. The major working load is taken by the pair of pre-loaded races at the mandrel nose end, and a single race is fitted to take the relatively light load at the tail end. This is free to float endwise in its housing and is spring-loaded to take up end play due to mandrel expansion. The drive to the mandrel in this case is through gears, but the same arrangement can be used where pulleys for belt drive is fitted. Rigid and precisely aligned housings are necessary for success with roller bearings, and a partially or completely enclosed box type headstock is to be preferred.

FIG. 3–6: Tailstock of Myford Super 7 lathe showing I base clamp 2 barrel clamp and 3 offset adjustment screws

Tailstock Design

One of the most essential features in the design of the tailstock is that it must be capable of exact axial alignment with the headstock, and also of being moved in a true axial line. Various ways are employed of clamping the tailstock to the bed, and it is generally desirable to avoid the need for tools in carrying out this operation. In some lathes the barrel is bored right through, with a tapered socket for the centres at the front end; it is keyed to prevent rotation in its housing, and threaded externally, for operation by an internally threaded handwheel, located endwise in the back of the housing, This is the type employed on the Myford ML 7 lathe, shown in Fig. 3–5; the bore of the barrel is equal to that of the mandrel, and the socket takes No. 2 Morse taper shanks in each case. This is convenient for dealing with long bars up to $\frac{7}{16}$ in. diameter. A locking device which does not displace the barrel to

FIG. 3–5: Myford ML7 tailstock, with lever clamp and offset adjustment

cause misalignment of its centre, is fitted to the housing.

Most modern lathes are provided with means of moving the tailstock sideways (at right angles to the lathe axis) in order to enable taper turning to be carried out between centres or to correct errors of alignment. A sub-base is usually fitted to the tail-stock casting, with a gib or key to prevent it getting out of parallel alignment when moved, and screws at front and back for adjustment and locking. Clamping of the ML 7 tail-stock is by means of an eccentric cam, operated by a hand lever. The base of the tailstock has a tongue on the underside with an adjusting gib to fit the central groove of the bed.

A different arrangement of the tailstock barrel feed is used on the Super 7 lathe, in which the rear end of the barrel is internally screwed, and operated by a screw on which the handwheel is mounted. Specially

FIG. 3–7: Saddle of Myford Super 7 lathe

FIG. 3–8: Saddle of Boxford 4½ lathe

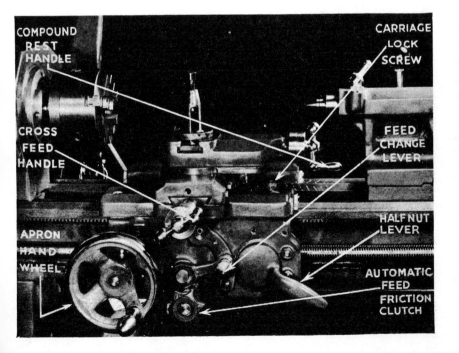

sensitive operation is obtained by using a three-start thread on these parts, in conjunction with a ball thrust race in the back of the housing. Tailstocks having internally threaded barrels can be arranged to eject the centres when the barrels are fully retracted; this feature is therefore favoured by turners as it promotes quick operation. But with an open bore, through the barrel, centres can be ejected almost as easily by inserting a rod from the rear of the bore, and throwing it in sharply by hand. Fig. 3–6.

Overhang at the front of the barrel housing is useful, and often essential, to enable the tailstock centre or other tools to approach the chuck or live centre as closely as possible, without fouling the saddle or its slides. Offsetting of the main tailstock support towards the back of the lathe helps to give clearance for the top slide feed screw, when working close to the lathe axis on work of small diameter.

Saddle and Compound Slide

The provision of a saddle, or "carriage", which will slide under mechanical control over the effective working length of the bed, is general for self-acting and screwcutting lathes, though "plain" lathes, and those used for instrument and horological work, may have short saddles, which are clamped to the bed in the required position, and tool movements controlled by the top and cross slides only. The sliding saddle can be traversed by the lead screw, or by a separate feed screw (where fitted), either of which will provide automatic feed, or "self-act"; in addition, it is usual to provide rack and pinion movement for quick traversing by hand. These fittings are incorporated in an "apron" or motion plate fitted vertically to the front of the saddle.

In order to provide the maximum range of movement without detracting from the length and bearing area of the saddle, it is commonly made of H or ⊏ section in plan view, allowing part of its length to run past the tailstock and sometimes the headstock as well. A long bearing surface, in relation to width, is desirable to prevent any tendency to slew, within the limits of its working clearance, which occurs in a short saddle when traversed to left or right. The saddle carries a "compound" slide rest consisting of a cross slide which moves at a fixed right angle to the lathe axis, and a top slide mounted on a swivelling base. Some small lathes of simple

FIG. 3–9: Inside view of saddle apron on Boxford 4½ in. lathe

FIG. 3–10: Quick-change screwcutting gearbox on Myford Super 7 lathe

design do not have a fully compound slide rest, but only a single slide which can be swivelled to provide cross, parallel and angular movements.

The saddle on the Myford Super 7 lathe, shown in Fig. 3–7, illustrates typical features of design, including the cross slide feed handle (1), the graduated swivel base of the top slide (2), toolpost (3), swivel locking screw (4), top slide feed handle (5), saddle clamping screw (6), top and cross feed indices (7), rack feed handwheel (8), and lead screw clasp nut engagement lever (9). The apron of this lathe contains gearing for the rack feed, with oil bath, slides for the cam-operated halves of the clasp nut, and lubricators or self-oiling bearings for all moving parts.

The saddle equipment of the Boxford lathe is more elaborate, as it is provided with self-acting feed for the cross slide as well as the saddle; the various parts are indicated by lettering. It will be noted that on this lathe the positions of the rack handwheel and the clasp nut lever are reversed, compared to the previous example. There has been a good deal of controversy as to which arrangement is the better or more convenient, but much depends on individual technique in handling the controls. American-type lathes generally have the handwheel on the left; many British lathes favour the right-hand position. Fig. 3–8.

Viewed from the inner side of the apron, the gearing for the various motions of the Boxford lathe is shown in Fig. 3–9. The half-nuts to engage the lead screw in this case have a swinging motion, though still cam-operated from the outside lever. As the self-acting feed is not driven

through the clasp nut, the lead screw has a longitudinal keyway for driving the worm which selectively provides, through a worm wheel, friction clutch and feed change lever, the motion for either longitudinal or cross feed. The pinion on the handwheel shaft operates the rack movement through reduction gearing.

In all practical lathes, the design and fitting of the slides is of the utmost importance. Gib strips are provided for adjustment of clearance, and once properly set up, only need very infrequent attention unless their screws are loosened by vibration, but

FIG. 3–11: Gear train of Myford screwcutting gearbox

they should be carefully checked. Various ways of clamping the top slide base are employed, and usually provide means of pulling the slide firmly down on its seating. Many lathes, including the Myford and Colchester, have a broad flat cross slide with machined top surface, and provided with T-slots or other mounting arrangements for boring work on the saddle, or other attachments and fixtures. For lathes not equipped in this way, it is sometimes possible to obtain boring tables which can be fitted in place of the standard cross slide when required. There is no doubt that a boring table extends the scope of a lathe for purposes beyond that of straightforward turning.

Quick-change screwcutting gearboxes

Whether these are built into the structure of the lathe or made as attachments for simple screwcutting lathes, they generally work on similar mechanical principles. To cover the full range of standard fractional-inch pitches, they usually have a range from 8 to 48 t.p.i. inclusive, with further reduction to cover self-acting feeds. The Myford gearbox is driven through a train of gears which can be changed from screwcutting to self-acting feed by simple reversal of one of the intermediate gears, without the need to shift the gear spindles. It is, however, possible to vary the ratio of the gearbox drive if required, to deal with unusual or metric pitch threads.

CHAPTER 4

INSTALLATION AND DRIVING EQUIPMENT

THE installation of a lathe is hardly less in importance than its design and construction. Not only may its usefulness be restricted or impaired, but its accuracy may be destroyed, by slipshod methods of installation. Whether the lathe is mounted on a bench or on a stand specially designed for it, great care should be taken to see that it cannot possibly be distorted when bolted down. In some cases the mounting surface of the lathe stand is machined or ground truly flat, and should be levelled in both cross and lateral planes before fitting the lathe; but even this is of no avail if the feet of the stand do not rest on an even surface. The same applies to bench mounting, and if a wooden bench is employed, it should not only be initially flat and level, but should be checked occasionally to see that no warping has taken place.

Light lathes do not necessarily call for permanent foundations or emplacements, and often it is not possible to provide them. Where the lathe is installed in domestic buildings or lightly built workshops, it is best to avoid fixing any part of the machine or its driving equipment directly to walls, floor or ceiling, as this may result in transmitting noise and vibration to the structure. There is much to be said in favour of resting the stand or bench on resilient pads of medium hard rubber, but care

should be taken to see that they do not perish or squash out in the course of time. Some machine tools are now mounted while supported on levelling jacks, on pads of felt or other soft fibrous material, soaked in resin or glue, which hardens and provides a perfectly stable support.

The mode of installing a lathe is to a great extent influenced by the means available for driving it. In the past, lathes were often driven by hand, either by the operator himself or with the aid of an assistant. Some lathes have been produced with incorporated or attached gearing to be driven by the operator's left hand, while the slide rest or hand tools were manipulated by the right. Though there is no difficulty in applying sufficient power by this method, for lathes of small size, it obviously restricts manipulation to some extent, and methods of drive which leave both hands free are much more convenient, to say the least.

Treadle drive fulfils this condition, and also enables more power to be applied than is normally possible by hand. Up to a few years ago, it was by far the most popular method of driving all small lathes up to about 4 in. centres, and has even been used on lathes of 6 in. centres. It has been calculated that a man of normal physique can exert foot power up to about $\frac{1}{8}$ h.p. (5,500 ft. lb. per minute) for periods up to one hour or more at a time. A good deal of useful work can be carried out on a lathe within this limit, providing that the tools are properly sharpened and set, and that rate of metal removal is not the the most important consideration. Although lathes specifically intended for treadle drive are no longer produced, so far as is known, it is still possible to obtain treadle fittings, or "foot motors" as they are called, or complete metal lathe stands with a large flywheel crank and driving pulley, connected to a hinged plate or "stretcher" for foot operation.

There are still a few operators who prefer treadle operation, claiming that it gives better control for delicate operations; it certainly enables speed to be varied within fairly wide limits without the need for complicated belt shifting or other gear. Though inexperienced operators often find it fatiguing to treadle a lathe, it becomes much easier with practice, in a similar way to pedal cycling. The need to supply the power by one's own muscular effort soon shows up any lack of tool efficiency, and provides practical lessons on how to grind tools and set them to best advantage. For these reasons, treadle drive, though it may be obsolescent, should not be forgotten or disregarded; it may still be a useful solution to the problems of the small workshop where no mechanical power is readily available.

For industrial work, or even in amateur workshops, power drive often becomes a necessity when any substantial amount of work has to be done. Power installations up to well into the present century usually employed a single engine or motor to drive the complete set of lathes or other machine tools in a machine shop. The power was transmitted by a main belt to a lineshaft running the entire length of the machine line, and thence by subsidiary belts to countershafts which in turn drove individual machines. It was necessary to locate and line up the various units accurately, and to control them by belt-shifting or clutch gear. This system became obsolete when small but efficient electric motors became available for direct attachment to individual machines, but in spite of its disadvantages, it is not entirely beneath consideration where only one motor is available for driving two or more machines. In a small workshop, where only one machine is in use at a time, it is often more economical and convenient to be able to provide an auxiliary drive to other machines, such as a drill, power saw or grinder, without the expense of extra motors.

For several years now, the industrial policy of one motor per machine has been followed for the majority of lathes of all sizes in both professional and amateur workshops. This owes its success not only to the efficiency, convenience and cheapness of the small electric motor, but also to the modern V-belt drive, which dispenses with the need for long distances between shaft centres. Thus it enables the complete driving unit to be made in a compact form, and attached to the lathe to form a self-contained machine which can be located anywhere or transported *en bloc* if required. The "motorised" lathe has now become practically universal, at least where current from the mains is readily available.

For lathes up to about 4 in. (excluding heavy duty industrial types), ample driving power can be obtained from motors of $\frac{1}{2}$ h.p. or less. The modern "fractional-horse-power" motors are very reliable and easy to install, moreover they require very little attention to keep them in proper running order. Most places in Great Britain are served by the

National Grid, which supplies alternating current (a.c.) at 220 to 250 volts 50 cycles, and for domestic or small power circuits (as distinct from industrial power), at single phase. The simplest type of motor available for this supply, in powers from ⅛ to ½ h.p., is of the induction or so-called "squirrel cage" type, having no armature winding, commutator or brush contacts. The "split-phase" version of this type has two sets of windings on the stator, for starting and normal working. Both windings are employed for starting, but when nearly full speed is attained, the starting winding is cut out by means of a centrifugal switch in the rotor. This enables the motor to be controlled by a simple contact switch directly on the line, and most of these motors will run in either direction, by arranging for the starting winding connections *only* to be reversible. Special switches with multiple contacts, such as the Santon or Dewhurst types, are available for single-lever reversing control.

The split-phase motor is quite suitable for driving lathes and other machine tools, provided that they are not required to start on a heavy static load. As their starting torque is necessarily limited, and starting current is heavy, they should be started on as light a load as possible so that they attain full speed quickly. For increased torque, the "capacitor-start" type of induction motor, in which a condenser is employed to assist the effect of the starting winding, is recommended. Both motors run at a fairly constant speed under varying load conditions—usually an advantage for machine tool drives—but the speed cannot be controlled by the use of resistances or other regulators. The standard forms of motors are of the four-pole type, which run at 1,425 to 1,450 r.p.m., but two-pole motors with

speeds from 2,850 to 2,900 r.p.m. can be obtained for machines which have to run faster.

Other types of a.c. motors include the "repulsion-induction" type, which has armature windings and commutator, and is capable of reversing and speed control. It has no special advantages for driving lathes. "Shaded-pole" a.c. motors are generally only made in quite small sizes; they have a low power factor and limited starting torque in most cases. For direct current (d.c.) mains supply, commutator motors with series windings (for high starting torque) or shunt windings (for more constant speed) must be employed. The so-called "universal" motor, for either a.c. or d.c. supply, is a series-wound type which is generally confined to light duty at constant torque; its speed varies in proportion to the load in most cases.

For lathes up to about 2 in. centres, a ⅛ h.p. motor will supply ample power; a 3 in. lathe will need ¼ h.p., though lathes of larger size have been run comfortably on motors of this power. Obviously a great deal will depend on the nature of the load and the rate at which work is carried out. The power needed increases rapidly for lathes of 4½ in. upwards, and it is often recommended that the more powerful motors (over ¾ h.p.) should be run on three-phase power supply; this may be insisted upon by electricity supply authorities.

Nearly all general-purpose lathes need to be provided with means of varying the mandrel speed. The simplest method of doing this, when lathes are driven through belting either by treadle or power, is to provide a multiple-stepped or so-called "cone" pulley on the mandrel. The driving pulley (on the treadle wheel or countershaft) must be stepped in reverse order, to keep the

FIG. 4–1: Three-step V-belt drive on
Myford ML7 lathe, showing back gear
below mandrel and belt guard lifted

than they are designed for, there is a risk that they may be irreparably damaged by scoring or seizure of the mandrel, if the lubrication should fail. For short runs at high speed, it is practicable to use two-step pulleys for the primary drive from motor to countershaft; alternatively, it is possible to fit a two-speed motor. High mandrel speed, if used with due care and discretion, is very useful for turning parts of small diameter, drilling small holes, and polishing.

While stepped pulleys provide the simplest speed-changing method, and are entirely satisfactory for light work, they limit the power that can be transmitted, and with normal tension the belt may slip under heavy load. This is not altogether a bad thing, so long as the belt is not run for long in a slipping condition; it may act as a "safety valve" to prevent damage to the work or the tool in the event of an accidental overload. The ability to unship the belt, leaving the mandrel free, is useful when setting up, marking out and static balancing in the lathe. But in lathes intended to cope with maximum duty, more positive power drive is often required, and one method of obtaining it is by using the Powergrip type of belting, in conjunction with variable gears or other speed-changing mechanism. The larger sizes of lathes are often equipped with all-geared headstocks, which provide the utmost efficiency and facility in power transmission. But the gears have to be made to a very high standard of accuracy to work smoothly without vibration, and are necessarily expensive. They may restrict the adaptability of the lathe if it is used for purposes other than straightforward turning operations.

belt tension constant, and by shifting the belt from one step to another, the relative effective diameters of driving and driven pulleys can be varied, thus changing the speed ratio. It is usual to provide three or more steps on each of the pulleys; their relative sizes vary for different lathes. Fig. 4–1.

There is also a wide variation in the speed of lathes, and the speed range is generally designed to suit the kind of work most likely to be encountered. For a back-geared lathe of $3\frac{1}{2}$ in. centres, for instance, a range of six speeds between 30 and 650 r.p.m. is commonly provided, and this can be obtained by running the countershaft at about $\frac{1}{4}$ motor speed; such as by fitting a 2 in. pulley on the motor shaft and an 8 in. pulley on the countershaft. As a typical example, the speed range of the Myford ML 7 is 200, 357, and 640 r.p.m. (direct), and 35, 62, and 110 r.p.m. (back geared). Small lathes used mainly on bar work in readily machinable materials, and using high-speed tools, can be run with advantage at much higher speeds, up to 2,000 r.p.m. or more. But it should be remembered that lubrication becomes very important at high speed, and if lathes are run faster

Various kinds of driving mechanisms capable of providing speed changes have been applied to lathes. Most of these work on the well-tried principle of expanding pulleys, which has been used on machine tools for well over fifty years; this type was used on the Raglan 5-in. lathe. Other types, such as the Kopp gear, used on some of the Boxford lathes, consist of an enclosed gearbox with friction-contact elements running in oil. Either of these will give progressive or "stepless" variable speed over a fairly wide range without shifting gears or transferring belts from one pulley step to another.

A device which retains all the simple virtues of belt drive, yet provides instant and easy speed changes, is the Tri-Leva unit, which at present is available only for fitting to the Myford ML 7 lathe. It employs three belts, one for each step of the cone pulleys, which are brought individually into operation by jockey pulleys, operated by hand levers and cams. The belts not in use are held out of contact with the pulleys by traps at the top and bottom, so that dragging and abnormal belt wear are avoided. Either lever, when depressed to engage its particular belt, automatically trips the locking gear of the other two, so that they are disengaged. When all three are out of gear, the mandrel is completely free; by depressing two

FIG. 4–2: The Tri-leva unit, fitted to the Myford ML7 lathe, for instant selection of either of 3 speeds

at once (with the motor switched off) they provide a friction lock to the mandrel. Experience with this unit shows that it is fully reliable and conducive to long belt life, while the facility of operation encourages the operator to use the most suitable speed for the job in all cases. It is, of course, operative for both direct and back gear speeds.

Friction clutches are fitted to many countershaft-driven lathes, and are very useful for control of the mandrel drive, as an alternative to switching the motor on and off each time. Sometimes the belt tension control lever is used to serve as a clutch, but this is not generally recommended, as the belt may drag and cause local wear. The use of a clutch helps to save wear and tear of motor switch contacts, and also assists "inching" of the mandrel when setting up work, or checking its concentricity.

Opinions are divided as to whether lathes should be provided with means of reversing the direction of mandrel rotation. Apart from certain specialised types of lathes, the cutting action is always in one direction, but for certain purposes, such as running

the saddle back to its starting point in screwcutting operations, the reverse gear is very useful. However, there is a risk that screwed-on chucks and other fittings may be slackened or run off when the lathe is reversed, and care must be taken to see that this does not occur. A positive form of mandrel nose fitting, such as the Camlock, now standard on many types of lathes, offers a means of preventing this occurrence. Chucks made by Burnerd and other makers can be fitted with Camlock drive, and an adaptor for the lathe mandrel nose is shown in Fig. 4–3.

Back Gearing

The lower range of speeds necessary for dealing with large castings and similar work can most conveniently be obtained by means of simple reduction gearing, which in the great majority of cases, is obtained by means of a layshaft at the back of the lathe mandrel. Other positions, however, are equally practicable, such as in Myford ML 7 and Super 7 lathes, where it is below the mandrel, and it can also be fitted inside the mandrel pulley, in the form of a quasi-epicyclic gear train. Except for this type, the layshaft gears are usually brought into action by eccentric or sliding action. The drive from the pulley to the mandrel can be disengaged, and a pinion attached to the pulley meshed with a large gear on the layshaft, which also carries a pinion. This in turn meshes with a large gear, generally known as the bull wheel, positively keyed to the mandrel. When direct drive is required, the layshaft gears are taken out of mesh, and the pulley is coupled to the bull wheel by a clutch

FIG. 4–3: Adaptor for Camlock chuck mounting on lathe mandrel nose

or equivalent device. All-geared head-stocks incorporate the back gear in the main gearbox.

Many substitutes for back gear have been devised for simple lathes, including double countershaft drives, but the torque which can be transmitted by any form of belt drive is limited, and toothed gears, or chain and sprocket drive, is much more efficient in this respect. The back gearing is generally designed to provide a reduction of 5 or 6 to 1 from the driving pulley.

CHAPTER 5

ACCESSORY EQUIPMENT

LATHES are generally supplied with certain basic accessories as part of their standard equipment. These include one faceplate, one catchplate, a pair of point centres, a set of change wheels, and sometimes a set of spanners, keys or other tools required for essential purposes. In the case of motorised lathes, the countershaft and motor platform are usually an integral part of the complete lathe assembly, and the same applies to stands or pedestals which contain driving mechanism. Otherwise, separate countershafts or extraneous fittings of any kind are classed as extra equipment.

The lathe faceplate is usually made as large in diameter as will comfortably swing over the bed or in the gap. It is provided with slots to take bolts for clamps or other holding fixtures, and these should be located to provide maximum latitude of location adjustment. The common

practice of arranging the slots radially is not the best arrangement in this respect, but it helps to keep the faceplate in fair balance, and this is important when lathes are run at high speed. Rigidity and true running of the faceplate are essential for accurate work, and it is generally made as a substantial casting, reinforced by ribs and a wide rim, also a boss to fit the mandrel nose, by screwing on or other approved method, to provide a true register. A similar but smaller casting is used for the catchplate, which needs to be provided with only a single radial slot for fixing the driving pin. Special forms of catchplates are sometimes used, with indexing arrangements for cutting multi-start threads or other devices; they may sometimes be combined with chucking fixtures or serve as auxiliary faceplates.

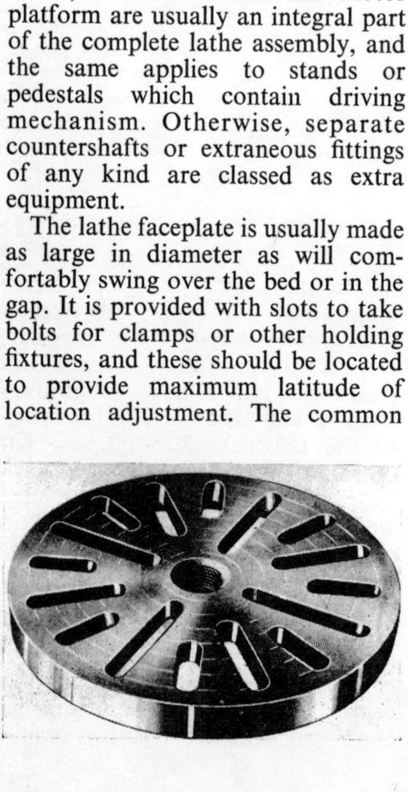

Standard point centres are made to fit the sockets of the mandrel and tailstock, and have conical points at 60 degrees included angle (A). Several forms of supplementary centres are used for special purposes, including a cutaway or half-centre (C) the object of which is to allow the lathe tool to approach the centre of the work as closely as possible when facing the end, or turning down to small diameter. This centre should not be cut away right to a

FIG. 5–1: 9 in. faceplate as fitted to Myford ML7 and Super 7 lathes

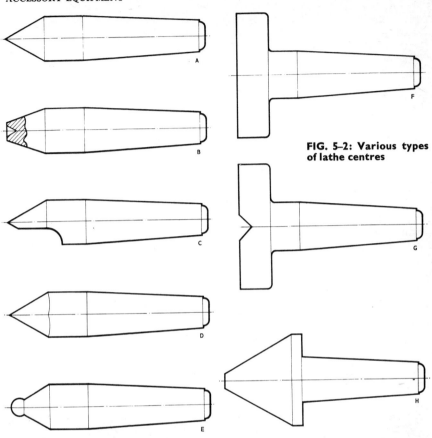

FIG. 5–2: Various types
of lathe centres

semicircle, but should leave sufficient of its point intact to seat properly in a drilled centre, and not produce a cutting or scraping action. Hollow centres (B) are necessary for dealing with work which cannot be centre-drilled, but which may have, or be provided with, a conical end as an alternative, such as spindles or small pivots. A form of centre which is not obtainable ready made, but may be found useful in certain circumstances, is one having a hardened ball formed at the tip (E). This will seat in chamfers or countersunks which are not at the correct 60 degree angle, but the area of contact provided by the ball is very small and it should

not be used for heavy work. Large diameter cone centres (H) are used to deal with hollow work, and are made with heads of various sizes. Drill pads, with either flat or V-grooved faces (F and G) are useful for fitting to the tailstock when drilling flat or round work from the headstock chuck. Sometimes they are provided with means of clamping the work in position. The drill pads supplied by lathe makers, while undoubtedly useful, are usually on the small size, and might well be increased in diameter. Myford's supply a form of combined drill pad and hollow centre, with loose heads having flat and V-grooved faces. It is also possible to obtain a taper-shanked adaptor, with the head screwed to correspond with the lathe mandrel nose, and this can be used to carry a faceplate, catchplate or chuck. Centres with hardened, square-cornered cones, or better still, with cutting teeth (D), can be used to clean up or correct the truth of drilled centres.

Several types of tools are held in the taper sockets of the head and tailstock, including drills, reamers, and die or tap holders, having shanks to correspond with those of the lathe centres. Centre drills may with advantage be fitted in a stub holder, which has the minimum overhang from the tailstock socket, and thereby provides greater rigidity than when it is held in an ordinary drill chuck. In all cases, the taper shanks of these fittings should fit the sockets accurately, and be free from dirt or swarf when inserted. It should never be necessary to drive them into the sockets; they should be pushed in

smartly by hand, and further end thrust produced in working should seat them firmly enough to withstand normal torque. If not, it indicates either that the tapers do not mate properly, or that they are prevented from making contact by the presence of burrs, bruises, scores, general roughness, or foreign matter.

The shanks should never be so tight a fit in the sockets as to cause them to jam, so that excessive force is necessary to extract them. In lathes with hollow mandrels and tailstocks, a rod can be inserted to push the shank out, using its momentum alone; no hammering or other heavy impact should be necessary. Many lathes have internal-screw tailstock barrels which eject the taper shanks when they are fully retracted. Should these for any reason become too tight for extraction by either method, the application of a little penetrating oil, and gentle heating by a cloth soaked in hot water, and wrapped round the end of the barrel, is recommended in preference to more forcible measures.

FIG. 5–3: Fixed and travelling steadies mounted on Myford Super 7 lathe

FIG. 5–4: Burnerd light duty 4 jaw chuck, made in sizes from 5 in. to 10 in. diameter

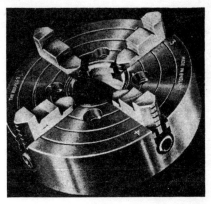

Steadies of various kinds are applied in lathe work to support shafts or other long pieces which lack inherent rigidity. The most common of these is the fixed steady, which is usually made with three radially adjustable pads, and is therefore usually called a three-point steady. For general work of not too long a duration, bronze or soft metal pads in running contact with the work, are satisfactory if kept well lubricated, but for heavier duty, hardened steel pads or rollers may be fitted. It is useful to hinge the top half of the steady frame, so that work may be inserted or removed without retracting the pads. The steady is mounted on the lathe bed by a suitable form of clamp, depending on the design of the bed, and the frame should be located concentric to the lathe axis when in position. It is important that the pads, when adjusted, should also guide the work in concentric alignment, and not force it out of its true running centre.

Travelling steadies are mounted on the lathe saddle, so that they move with the cutting tool, as close to it as practicable. They usually have one or more hardened pads, adjustable to make contact with the work, but rollers, or fibre pads, are sometimes used. Some steadies employ a single pad with a V-notch on the end, fitted to be both horizontally and vertically adjustable. The steady may either precede or follow the tool, as may be most convenient for the particular operation. If it precedes the tool, the surface on which it bears must be smooth and run truly, otherwise any error will deflect the work, and affect the truth of the surface produced by the tool. For this reason, it is generally preferable to use a following steady where

possible. Sometimes special tools incorporating steadies are employed, as in the box type or running-down tool, which is mostly used in quantity production. If more than one cut is taken when using a travelling steady, it is necessary to readjust the pads to compensate the reduction of work diameter. This does not apply when cutting long threads, at least while the crest diameter is intact, but the presence of burrs thrown up at the thread flanks may interfere with smooth working contact with the steady pads, and they should not be allowed to build up. Fig. 5–3

The use of chucks with radial sliding jaws, stepped to hold work of a wide diametric range, either externally or internally, is now practically universal on all metal turning Two general types of chucks are employed, one having the jaws (usually four in number) individually adjustable by means of screws, Fig. 5–4, while the other is commonly made with three jaws, operated simultaneously to co-ordinate their radial adjustment—in other words to be "self-centring". This type of chuck is much the simpler to manipulate for work which is smooth and symmetrical, and this applies to round and hexagonal bar stock, and parts that have already been pre-machined to these shapes.

FIG. 5–5 Cutaway view of Burnerd 3 jaw
self-centring chuck, showing scroll and
operating pinion

The jaws of the self-centring chuck
are machined to slide in T-slots, and
with teeth at the back to engage the
grooves of a spirally machined scroll.
This may be rotated in the chuck
body by bevel gearing, with pinions
having sockets to take a square key
or other form of wrench, as shown
in the cutaway sectioned chuck,
(5–5). Alternatively, in some of the
smaller self-centring chucks the scroll
is operated by an external ring,
either knurled for a hand grip or
provided with holes for the insertion
of a tommy bar, or notched for the
engagement of a C-spanner or other
form of lever.

The grip obtainable by the jaws of
a self-centring chuck, on work which
enables them to make good contact
over all or most of their length, is
sufficient for all normal machining
work, but may not be adequate when
only a short length of surface can be
gripped, or where the overhang
outside the jaws is excessive. Rough
castings or irregular-shaped parts
should not be held in this type of
chuck. The force which can be
exerted through the scroll and its
gearing is limited, but no attempt
should be made to augment it by
increasing the leverage over and
above that normally obtainable with
the chuck key supplied, as this may
result in over-straining the jaws or
the scroll and thus putting the chuck
permanently out of truth.

Independent-jaw chucks can be
used for a much wider range of work
than the self-centring type, and the
grip obtainable through the screws
is greater than that of a scroll. But
their use entails a setting-up operation, in which each jaw must be
separately adjusted to a delicacy
depending on the degree of concentric
accuracy required. This adjustment
may in certain circumstances be
rather tedious, and many operators
grudge the time which it involves,
preferring to use the self-centring
chuck wherever possible, even though
the nature of the work may make it
inappropriate. Various aids to accurate setting-up may be used, and
will be described later in this book.
Most castings, forgings, and non-
circular work of all kinds can be
dealt with in the four-jaw chuck, and
it is often the most suitable and

FIG. 5–6 Six-jaw Burnerd Grip-tru
chuck, with key in operation for micro-
adjustment

efficient means of mounting such work in the lathe; the only alternatives are clamping it directly to the faceplate or using special chucking fixtures.

The most popular chucks used on British lathes are those produced by F. Burnerd & Co. Since they were first made about half a century ago in a small factory at Putney, London, S.W., the demand for these chucks has rapidly increased, and they are now manufactured in a large and highly organised and equipped factory at Winchester. The present range of products includes three-jaw and four-jaw chucks in sizes from 2½ in. (62 mm.) to 28 in. (710 mm.) diameter, besides several other types of chucks, all made to a high degree of precision to keep pace with the exacting requirements of modern engineering practice.

Up to comparatively recent years, it was generally considered that self-centring chucks should not be expected to work to very fine limits of concentric accuracy; a chuck which would hold work with not more than 0·003 in. error at 1 in. from the jaws, when new, was considered pretty good. The maintenance of this degree of accuracy was dependent on the durability of its wearing parts, and the care exercised in its use. Burnerd chucks are now made to finer limits of initial accuracy, and of materials which ensure that this is better maintained, provided that they are not abused. The Griptru self-centring chucks incorporate a special adjustment device which enables minor errors to be corrected down to a limit of 0·0002 in. of concentricity. They are made with either three or six jaws, the latter having advantages

in enabling fragile objects such as rings or thin tubes to be held securely without risk of marking or distortion. Fig. 5–6.

Other types of Burnerd self-centring chucks are made with jaws having detachable and reversible faces, which avoid the need for two sets of jaws, and also allow soft faces to be fitted and machined in position to suit special work. All Burnerd three-jaw and four-jaw chucks can now be supplied to fit directly on the lathe mandrel nose, and dispense with the need for backplates or adaptors, for screw or other fitting methods conforming to British, American or German standards.

Chucks of any kind which are not arranged for direct mounting may need to have backplates specially machined and fitted. Castings are generally used, and should first of all be turned on the back face and boss, then bored out and internally threaded or otherwise machined to fit accurately on the register and shoulder face of the mandrel. The front face and spigot or other concentric register for the chuck should then be machined while the backplate is in position on the mandrel. Methods of fitting chucks and of securing them to the backplates, vary in different makes, and

FIG. 5–7 Burnerd chuck with detachable and reversible jaws.

the makers generally provide fitting instructions which should be carefully followed. Sometimes it is advocated that instead of close-fitting the spigot on the backplate, clearance should be allowed, so that if the chuck goes out of truth for any reason, it can be corrected by loosening the securing bolts and shifting it slightly as required. This method may be expedient in certain cases, but it is not approved by chuck manufacturers, as it impairs the security of the fitting and may put the chuck body out of balance.

Jaws of self-centring chucks are nearly always numbered or otherwise marked to show their position in relation to their fitting slots. When changing jaws, No. 1 jaw should be fitted first, with the scroll turned so that the entering end of the groove is just clear of the No. 1 jaw slot. After inserting the jaw as far as it will go, the scroll is turned in the closing direction to engage the teeth of the jaw, but no farther. No. 2 jaw is then inserted and the scroll similarly engaged, then followed by No. 3, taking care in each case that the jaws work smoothly in their slots and are in positive engagement. All working parts of chucks should be kept clean and sparingly lubricated. Chuck jaws are not interchangeable, but have to be selectively fitted when the chuck is made. If a jaw should become damaged or lost, it is not normally possible to obtain a spare jaw, or set of jaws, for replacement in the chuck body, though makers will sometimes undertake to make and fit new jaws at the works.

For the utmost accuracy in holding bar stock or other circular work of small diameter, collet chucks are usually employed, using split collets in a range of standard diameters. In small horological and instrument lathes, the mandrel nose is internally tapered to fit the collets, which are generally made with an angle of about 40 degrees inclusive. The collets are screwed on the tail end and are drawn into the taper bore by means of a draw tube which passes through the hollow mandrel and is operated by a handwheel at the tail end. For long bars, the size of work which can be held is limited to that admitted through the bore of the draw tube, but short pieces of larger size can be held in suitable collets, and they can be enlarged and stepped on the outside to hold thin discs or rings of still larger diameter.

It is also possible to use push-in collets operated by a screwed nose cap, and this is often done in the larger sizes of lathes. Where the mandrel socket is not bored to suit the taper of the collet, an adaptor sleeve may be fitted, or a nosepiece may be screwed on to the mandrel. This has the advantage of enabling long work up to the diameter of the mandrel bore to be admitted. Collet chucks enable finished work to be held securely without marking the surface, and though they are normally available only for circular work, they can be made to hold square, hexagonal or other special sections. Their major disadvantage is that individual collets will only hold

FIG. 5–8 Effect of holding oversize or undersize work in split collet chuck.

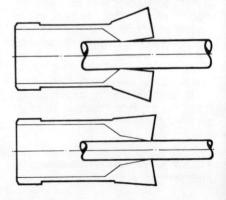

FIG. 5–9 A set of Myford No. 2 Morse collets, with insertion tool

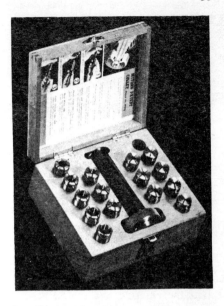

work within a narrow limit of their standard size; if either oversize or undersize stock is inserted, not only will the area of gripping surface on the work, but also the fit of the collet in its taper socket, become quite inadequate, and there is a risk of permanent distortion or other damage to the collet. This effect is shown in exaggerated form in Fig. 5–8.

A type of collet which, though still limited in respect of diametric latitude, gives a parallel grip over almost its full length, is that introduced by Myford's for use on ML 7 and Super 7 lathes. It does not require a special conical seating in the mandrel, or an external adaptor, as the collets fit the No. 2 Morse taper socket. The acute angle of this taper gives a very good gripping power when the collet is pushed in by a nosecap fitted to the mandrel nose thread, but the collets are not self-extracting, and this is often regarded as a serious objection to collets of this type. Myford's have overcome this by grooving the large end of the collets and springing them into the nosecap with the aid of a simple tool; they are then positively extracted when the nosecap is unscrewed. A set of Myford collets in sizes from $\frac{1}{16}$ in. to $\frac{1}{2}$ in. by $\frac{1}{32}$ together with their nosecap and inserting tool, is illustrated in Fig. 5–9.

Burnerd's have introduced a new type of collet chuck in which the gripping members consist of a number of metal strips, tapered on the outside and assembled together in radial formation in a slotted metal body. This has a much wider latitude of size and at all times has a truly parallel grip throughout its full length. Another feature of this chuck is that the front ends of the strips are stepped, so that they hold work right up to the face, and the closing cap is flush with the face to clear the tool in close-up operations. Fig. 5–10.

The Burnerd Multisize chuck, as it is called, is made in various sizes having maximum capacities from $\frac{3}{4}$ in. to $2\frac{1}{2}$ in. and each collet has a size latitude of $\frac{1}{8}$ in. The chuck assembly can be fitted to standard spindle noses of various types, and the closing cap is operated by a key with a bevel pinion, engaging a toothed ring on the back of the cap. A quick-acting lever-operated version, which can be opened or closed without stopping the lathe, and also one for air or hydraulic operation, are available. A lever-operated chuck for attachment to the mandrel nose, using standard collets of normal taper angle, is also produced by Myford's.

Chucks for holding drills or other tools, mostly in the lathe tailstock, are of various kinds, but the most popular, at least for small and moderate size lathes, is the Jacobs

FIG. 5–10 Burnerd Multisize collet unit

type, which is made in sizes to hold shanks of maximum size from $\frac{1}{4}$ in. upwards. This chuck has three inwardly inclined jaws, on which rack teeth are cut to engage an internally threaded ring; bevel gear teeth are provided on the lower end of the ring for operation by a pinion on the key, which also has a spigot on the end to engage radial holes in the body. These chucks are robust in construction, and will retain their truth indefinitely if used with reasonable care. They are made with taper sockets in the back of the body, to which taper shanks can be fitted, or sometimes to suit special methods of fitting. Fig. 5–13.

Simple and generally inexpensive types of screw drill chucks are satisfactory for light work but they do not hold drills very securely, and often their accuracy and durability are open to criticism. Drill chucks of all kinds are designed mainly to cope with axial load only, and they should not be used to hold work for turning operations, or milling cutters, which impose side loads of any magnitude.

FIG. 5–11 Assembly of Multisize collet chuck

Hand Rests

Although nearly all the work operations on metal turning lathes can best be carried out by the use of slide rest tools, the ability to use hand tools is an advantage for certain purposes, such as turning curved contours, rounding-off the ends of bolts, etc. Most lathe manufacturers supply hand rests adjustable for height, and fitted to sockets in brackets which can be clamped either to the bed, or to the cross slide after removing the swivelling slide. The hand rest, or T-rest as it is sometimes called, should be set as close to the work as possible, either parallel, square, or at any convenient angle, depending on the nature of the operation. Height setting is adjusted to suit the thickness of the tool and its cutting angle.

As an improvised substitute for a hand rest, it is customary to hold a flat bar of metal in the tool post of the lathe in the required position to support the hand tool. This is convenient for hand chasing and similar operations, but it restricts the manipulation of the tool for

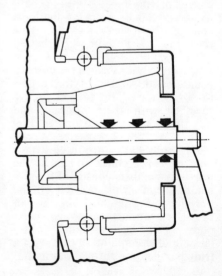

FIG. 5–12 Key-operated Multisize chuck with camlock fitting

other work, as the tool post is liable to get in the way. The standard form of hand rest may be found too long for use on short pieces mounted between centres, and short or specially shaped rests, adapted to fit the standard sockets, may have to be made to suit particular work. Fig. 5–14.

Clamping Appliances

For mounting work on the faceplate or cross slide of the lathe, various forms of clamps are employed. One of the most common of these is the slotted toe clamp shown at A (5–15). It is usually made in the form of a forging or a malleable casting, but can also be machined from solid steel if required. The narrow toe of the clamp is useful for gripping on relatively small surfaces, while the slotted part of the clamp provides adequate strength. This clamp requires packing of approximately the same thickness as the work, under the back end. To avoid the need for packing, the bent clamp, forged from flat steel (centre), is often employed but it can only be used for work approximately the same thickness as the bent heel, unless extra packing is employed. Much greater latitude can be obtained by the clamp shown on right, which has an adjustable jack screw at the back end. Clamps of special shape, including those having forked or otherwise shaped ends, may be found necessary for holding awkward workpieces.

The device known as a "faceplate dog", having a large head fitted with a cross screw, is rather uncommon nowadays, but it is extremely useful as a locating device and also for gripping work radially if it cannot readily be held over its outer face. A set of three or four of these dogs can be used as an improvised chuck, and a faceplate equipped in this way may well have been the progenitor of the modern four-jaw chuck. It is significant that this type of chuck was often called a "dog chuck" by turners of an earlier generation. For some kinds of work, pointed and hardened radial screws may be fitted to the dogs to penetrate the edges of castings, or fit pre-drilled indentations, thereby providing

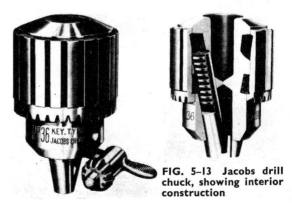

FIG. 5–13 Jacobs drill chuck, showing interior construction

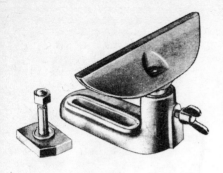

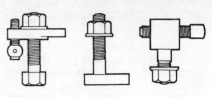

FIG. 5–15   Various forms of faceplate clamps

FIG. 5–14   Myford type hand rest, adjustable for height

greater security than frictional grip alone. Fig. 5–15 .

The term "strap" as applied to workshop appliances is generally taken to mean a flat or ribbed bar with holes at each end, to span work pieces and enable them to be secured by bolts. Sometimes the shape of the strap is adapted to suit the work, such as by providing a concave or V-notched bearing surface. In any case, it must be sufficiently rigid to resist bending when the bolts are normally tightened. Various other clamping appliances are called for in dealing with special mounting problems, and may be developed to serve as semi-permanent jigs or machining fixtures. A selection of bolts and nuts is necessary for use with clamping appliances, and however great their number and variety, are hardly ever more than barely adequate to cope with practical requirements.

Other lathe accessories found necessary in general work include angle plates, parallel packings in various thicknesses, V-blocks and V-packing strips. Some of these are obtainable as standard items, but others may have to be made or adapted as and when required. Their design and application will be further described in chapters dealing with particular operations.

Feed Screw Indices

Nearly all modern lathes are equipped with graduated indices to the cross and top slide feed screws, either as a standard fitting or as an optional extra. In lathes up to 3½ in. centre height, a good deal of traversing work is often carried out by the lead screw operation of the saddle, and a handwheel may be fitted to the outer end for this purpose, also with a graduated index. It is usual to graduate the index, in conjunction with the pitch of the feed screw, to read in increments of 1 /1,000 in. Thus the index for a feed screw of 10 t.p.i. is graduated in 1/100ths, and for a lead screw of 8 t.p.i., in 1/125ths. It should be noted that the cross slide index represents *radial* movements, and therefore the reading on the index is doubled in relation to *diametric* dimensions.

Direct measurement to a moderate degree of accuracy can be carried out by either feed screw index, provided that backlash is taken up in one direction. But as the screws are subjected to wear, they may not always retain their accuracy under working conditions. Their most useful function is in minor comparative measurements; for instance, if it is found necessary to reduce the diameter of the work by 0·010 in., this may be roughly equal to five divisions on the cross slide index, and error in this respect is likely to be on the minimum side, unless spring or deflection of the tool needs to be taken into account.

Indices may be fixed directly to the feed screw, or fitted with a frictional mounting so that they can be set to zero at any position of the screw. This is a great convenience in counting the required number of divisions, provided that the index can be relied upon to stay where set, but if it is erratic or liable to shift when the screw is rotated, it is worse than useless. The size of the index disc or rim is important; if it is too small it may be difficult to read properly, and where conditions permit, a large, open scale is obviously to be preferred. Some lathes have been fitted with disc handwheels to all screws, which can be graduated directly on the edge, but the general tendency in modern lathes is to use balanced ball handles for convenience in manipulation, and these need to be fitted with separate indices.

It is usual to graduate the base of the swivelling slide in degrees, and this is convenient for setting it for bevel or taper turning, but the size of circular base which can normally be fitted is inadequate for precision of angular setting, and it is generally necessary, or at least prudent, to take test cuts on the work and check the angle with a protractor, or by application of a taper gauge or matching component. Acute tapers are difficult to measure accurately, but may be tested by making longitudinal chalk or pencil marks at intervals around the external part. On applying the mating part and partially rotating it, the marks should be wiped or erased over the full contact length, or if error is present, will clearly show the high spots.

A longitudinal scale on the tailstock barrel gives a very useful indication of depth when drilling holes, or using facing and counterboring cutters. It is handier and more positive than using a rule or other gauge on the outside of the barrel, and the finer increments of movement can, if required, be measured by indexing the tailstock handwheel.

CHAPTER 6

TOOLS AND TOOL HOLDERS

THE single-point tools used for metal turning differ from most other kinds of cutting tools, especially those for working on wood or other relatively soft materials. They need to be strong and rigidly mounted, to withstand heavy bending stresses imposed in cutting hard and tough materials. The acute angles employed for ordinary edge tools would be too weak to stand up to attrition, and to impact or vibration, to which they are often subjected. They need to be as hard as possible, without being brittle enough to cause risk of chipping or breakage of the cutting edge. The nature of the tool steel, the shape of the cutting edges, and the way they are presented to the work, are all of the utmost importance in metal turning.

It is possible to obtain ready made lathe tools of all shapes and sizes, and they are often supplied in sets which cover most normal requirements. These may comprise two side tools (right- and left-hand), three round-nose tools (straight, right- and left-hand offset) one boring tool, one each external and internal screw-cutting tools, and one parting tool; nine tools in all. It may be necessary to duplicate some of these tools when different materials, requiring modification of cutting angles, have to be dealt with; and the shape of the cutting edges may also have to be varied to suit the contour of the work. Fig. 6–1.

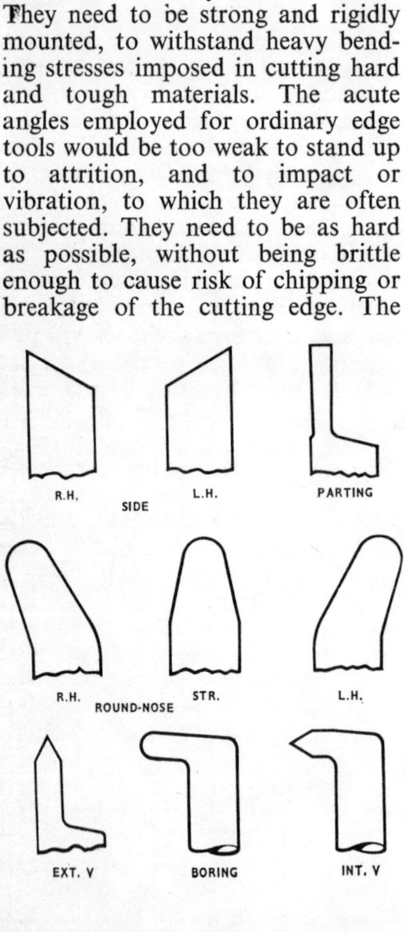

Tool Steels

In common with most other kinds of cutting tools, lathe tools were formerly made from carbon steel, the shape of which was mainly formed by forging, prior to hardening, tempering and grinding. This steel was generally satisfactory for moderate rates of machining, but for heavy work or high speed, in which heat was generated by friction, the edge of the tool was liable to lose its

R.H.   L.H.   PARTING
SIDE

R.H.   STR.   L.H.
ROUND-NOSE

EXT. V   BORING   INT. V

FIG. 6–1 Basic types of lathe tools (plan views)

temper, or in other words, to become softened, so that temporarily at least, it was made useless. Moreover, the same result was produced if care was not taken in grinding it. The advent of "high-speed" steel, which retained its temper, even when heated to very high temperature, enabled lathes to work at much higher feeds and speeds than were formerly possible, with a consequent increase of output. Carbon steel has therefore been entirely superseded in modern industrial practice, but it is not completely obsolete for light work. When special small tools are required, the ability to anneal, machine or forge carbon steel is often an advantage. The grade of carbon steel known as silver steel (though it contains no silver) is readily obtainable, and can be machined fairly easily while in the semi-annealed state, as supplied. It can be hardened by heating to redness and quenching in water or thin oil, and tempered to the required hardness by controlled re-heating. Details of the heat treatment for all kinds of tool steels can be found in the handbook *Hardening and Tempering Engineers' Tools*.

The modern high speed tool steels contain, in addition to carbon, a certain percentage of metallic elements such as tungsten, cobalt or vanadium. Besides being resistant to softening at any temperature likely to be encountered in normal service, these steels have a high tensile strength, and retain their cutting edge better than carbon steel under conditions of attrition or abrasion, such as encountered in dealing with materials of difficult machining quality, or impregnated with sand or scale.

When high speed steel tools were first introduced, they were often made from solid bars, which were forged to shape in the same way as carbon steel, though with greater difficulty, and hardened by quenching from yellow heat in oil, or sometimes in an air blast. The greater expense of high speed steel, and the uncertainty of results obtained by these methods, soon led to its use in prehardened state, and greater economy, by elimination of waste entailed by making the tools in solid bars. At the present day, the general practice is to apply the tool steel in small pieces, attached in various ways to shanks or holders of mild or low carbon steel.

Composite Tools

In some cases, the pieces of tool steel, of appropriate shape, and large enough to provide for a reasonable amount of re-grinding, are brazed or resistance-welded to the shanks, to form in effect a solid tool. Alternatively, small tool bits in the form of square, rectangular or round bars, may be clamped in holders provided with sockets or seatings to receive them. The hardest and most resistant cutting material, other than diamonds, at present available is known as tungsten carbide, and by reason of its special nature, it is most conveniently produced in powder form, which is pressed to shape in dies and solidified by a sintering process. The tips thus produced are generally brazed to shanks, and the term "tipped" tool is generally taken to mean one in which the tip is of tungsten carbide, but it can also apply to tools with tips of other kinds of tool steel. Where diamond tipped tools are employed, the object is usually high precision and freedom from wear, rather than heavy duty.

For most lathe operations, the high speed tool steels now obtainable under various trade names give excellent service if properly ground, securely mounted and adjusted to correct height. Tungsten carbide cannot be used to its fullest advantage on small, light lathes; its proper sphere is in heavy duty industrial machines, working at maximum feeds and speeds. It can be applied to deal with an abnormally hard casting, or other intractable materials which impose heavy wear on the more common steels, but it calls for extreme care when impact or intermittent cutting is involved, and vibration must at all costs be avoided. Tungsten carbide cannot be ground on ordinary grinding wheels, but calls for a special grade of abrasive wheel, and to obtain the best results, the cutting edge should subsequently be lapped with a diamond-impregnated wheel or hand slip. But subject to these conditions, one or two tungsten carbide tipped tools can be found very useful in any workshop.

The forged lathe tools which were formerly employed were often made with a dropped bend or "swan neck" at the end, for dealing with steel or other tough materials. It is probable that this shape was largely a hangover from the old "heel tool" used before slide rests were generally available. In this primitive type of tool, the underside of the tool, resting on a flat tool rest, was used as a fulcrum to apply leverage against the cutting load. But even when this was no longer necessary, the particular shape of the tool remained popular, and under certain conditions, its resilience could be used to advantage to avoid overloading or digging-in of the tool point. In modern practice, however, it is inconvenient to forge tools to this shape, and the swan-necked form of tool has become practically extinct; the general practice nowadays is to make the tool and its mounting as rigid as possible. It would obviously be impossible to make the popular form of tool bit or its holder with a bend of this kind.

Tool Bits

Small high speed tool bits are generally made in short lengths, of square section, with the sides surface ground, and the ends cut off obliquely, so that the minimum amount of grinding is required to shape them into right- or left-hand side tools. For other forms of tools, more extensive grinding is necessary, but a wide range of operations can be carried out with side tools, either with a sharp angle at the front, or radiused to a greater or less extent. The tool steel can also be obtained in greater lengths, with hot-rolled finish, and in round bits for use in boring bars and similar tools. Deep section tool bits, with the sides tapered for clearance, are available for mounting in special holders, and have largely superseded solid tools for parting-off operations. These require only to be ground on the front face, and the standard length of blade is sufficient for deep parting, and many regrindings, before it becomes too short for use.

Tool bits of $\frac{3}{8}$ in. square section or larger can be held directly in the toolpost of a small lathe, but the more popular size of bit is $\frac{1}{4}$ in. or less, held in a holder which generally has an inclined socket providing some measure of height adjustment, and also pre-set top take. This eliminates or reduces the need for grinding the top face of the tool bit, which after a few regrindings would be liable to weaken it. The common form of tool holder for small tool bits is that shown in Fig. 6–2, in which the angle of the bit is exaggerated to illustrate how it provides both top rake and variation of height at the cutting edge by adjusting its projection from the holder. Such holders are facile, but by no means ideal.

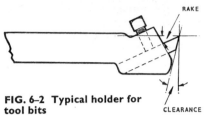

RAKE

CLEARANCE

FIG. 6–2 Typical holder for tool bits

They are generally designed particularly to fit the lantern type of tool post, and the deep section of the shank often gives too high a tool level to suit other types of tool posts. The use of a single screw to hold the bit is also open to objection, as unless the socket is accurately formed, it may not locate the bit properly. Some of the cheaper holders of this type have the sockets formed by hot drifting, which leaves so rough a surface that the tool bits are over-stressed, and may even be broken, when the set screw is tightened. The sockets should be accurately broached, and should really fit the tool bit at the sides, but this is hardly practicable, because the bits are not usually ground to close accuracy on all sides. Side clearance is liable to allow the tool bit to shift to a limited extent when subjected to heavy side load. These holders are made with straight, left- and right-hand offset heads; it is usually necessary to use a left-hand holder to get close to the lathe chuck, or to a broad shoulder on the work, unless the shank is slewed at a fairly large angle to the left in the tool post.

Several other kinds of holders for tool bits have been devised, and some of them have been commercially produced, but their usefulness is influenced by the design of the main tool fixture, or tool post, as it is generally called. Whether small tool bits in holders, solid, composite or tipped tools, are used, it is important that they should be held securely in the tool post, and that the latter should give some facility for swivelling or other adjustment.

Rake and Clearance Angles

The cutting efficiency of lathe tools is largely dependent on the shape of their cutting edges, and in particular, the angles to which these are ground. These again are subject to modification to suit the material to be machined. Attempts are often made to lay down rigid rules for cutting angles, but there are so many materials used in engineering practice nowadays that it is hardly practicable to keep sets of tools ground to suit all of them, and it is both tedious and wasteful to grind tools to ideal shape each time different materials have to be dealt with. Hardly any two experienced turners agree precisely on the cutting angles which they consider most suitable for particular jobs. It is more important to know *why* variations in this respect are desirable, and having found that this holds good in practice, always to maintain these angles properly when re-grinding tools.

All normal tools require *clearance* to enable the tool edge to penetrate the surface of the work as it is fed in to produce the required cutting action. In order to maintain the maximum strength at the cutting edge, this angle should be as small as possible, but a tool with too fine

FIG. 6–3 Straight and offset tool bit holders by Jones & Shipman Ltd.

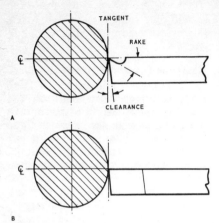

FIG. 6–4 Diagrams illustrating rake and clearance angles

a clearance will fail to cut as soon as the slightest wear of the edge has taken place. The need to hone a tool to improve the finish, or restore the keenness of a slightly blunted tool, may affect the amount of clearance necessary. From 5 to 10 degrees to the vertical line will be found satisfactory for most operations. Most jobbing turners tend to use larger clearance angles than are really necessary, but this is not a major disadvantage unless maximum tool life under heavy cutting is required.

The term "rake" has been defined in various ways, but it is usually taken to mean the angle of the top face of the cutting edge, relative to the horizontal, or more correctly, the radial line of the tool. The diagram (Fig. 6–4(a)), shows a tool ground from solid steel, having fairly normal front clearance and considerable top rake. This reduces the load involved in penetrating the work surface and is generally conducive to efficiency, but it also weakens the edge and cannot be universally employed, for various reasons. The tool shown in Fig.

6–4(b) has the top edge ground in line with the horizontal line, in other words, it has no top rake.

For dealing with tough, fibrous materials which tend to leave the tool in a long, curly chip or coil, various degrees of top rake can be employed with advantage. The most common angle is about 10 degrees, and this is suitable for many kinds of steel, also drawn bronze and gunmetal, and rolled or drawn aluminium alloys. Free-cutting mild steel may be machined at 15 degrees top take, and angles up to 30 degrees can be used on copper, some kinds of plastics, and sometimes for fine finishing or "shaving" cuts on steel shafts, rollers or other plain cylindrical surfaces. Metals of a more brittle nature, which tend to come off in short chips or splinters, such as castings in iron or brass, some kinds of aluminium, or brass "screw rod", call for a smaller rake angle, or none at all.

Both the rake and clearance angles are influenced by the height at which the tool is set in relation to the centre of the work. The effect of raising or lowering the tool is shown in Fig.

FIG. 6–5 Effect of tool height on cutting angles

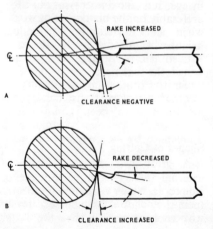

6–5, where it will be seen that with the tool above centre (A), the effective rake is increased, while the clearance is decreased and may even become negative so that the tool will not cut. On the other hand, setting the tool below centre (B) will decrease the top rake and increase the clearance so that the tool has a scraping rather than a cutting action. As a general rule, tools should always be set with the edge as nearly on the centre line of the work as possible; and for facing cuts, deviation from this height will prevent the tool from cutting right to the centre of a blank disc. For certain special purposes, tools designed to be set above the centre line, or to be fed on the tangent line of the work, are employed; but it will be evident that these can only work properly on work of one diameter without re-setting, so that their application is greatly restricted.

Several appliances, some of them very ingenious, have been devised for setting lathe tools exactly to centre height, but it is significant that these are rarely used by turners when once some experience in lathe operation has been acquired. The usual practice is to set the tool as closely as possible to centre height by eye, and take one or two trial cuts, preferably on the blank face of work, when any deviation from centre height will immediately be apparent. Adjustment of height may be obtained by slips of metal packing under the tool, or by using one of several quick-setting tool post devices.

Shapes of Cutting Tools

A great deal of the work on external surfaces can be done with side tools, which are capable of both facing and traversing operations without re-setting. The tool generally referred to as a "right-hand" side tool has its side cutting face on the *left* and is generally fed or traversed mainly to the left as well. It is much more widely used than the "left-hand" side tool, to which the reverse applies. The side cutting faces in both types of tools are ground to give clearance; and rake, where used, is ground at right angles to this face. Except where it is necessary to produce a sharp internal angle adjacent to a shoulder in turned work, it is not generally desirable to use a tool with a sharp corner on the cutting edge. A slight radius ground or honed on the corner will help to relieve local loading on the tool edge, and also to produce a better finish on the work. The example of a side tool in the diagram Fig. 6–6 has this radius shown exaggerated. For shafts or other parts of machinery which are liable to encounter working stress, sharp internal corners are to be avoided where possible, as they provide a focus for fatigue cracks or fractures. The usual practice is to provide a "fillet" or internal radius at the shoulder.

Sometimes side tools have a short part of the front edge ground with a "land" or flat, parallel to the axis of

FIG. 6–6 Right hand side tool with radius at tip

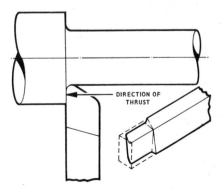

DIRECTION OF THRUST

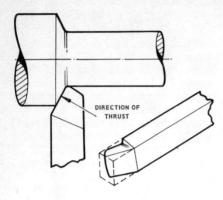

the work, with a view to improving finish on traversing cuts, by wiping or burnishing out tool marks. This is common practice in side tools used for "running down" bolts or similar parts in a single deep cut with fine traversing feed. For facing operations on steel or brass, some turners prefer a side tool which is narrow enough to allow a slight flexibility or "spring" when taking a wide finishing cut. Rapid roughing down or "ripping" on readily machinable steel or other metals can be done very effectively by means of a tool with its side face ground at an angle, up to about 30 degrees as shown in Fig. 6–8.

Round-nosed tools are suitable for traversing cuts on straight shafts without shoulders or collars, and if

FIG. 6–8 Round-nosed tool in use on traversing cut.

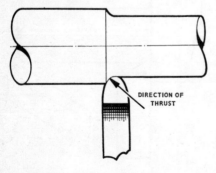

FIG. 6–7 Deep cutting or ripping tool with angular face

ground with top rake in the usual way, they will cut with equal efficiency when traversed in either left-hand or right-hand direction. They are sometimes traversed backwards and forwards by using the tumbler or other feed reversing gears and fed in for each pass until the work is reduced to correct size. But as it is not usually desirable to reverse the feed while the lathe is in motion, this method is not so expeditious as it seems. If properly ground and set, round-nosed tools are capable of producing a high finish, without visible tool marks. But if either the tool or the work is not rigidly

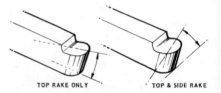

TOP RAKE ONLY   TOP & SIDE RAKE

FIG. 6–9 Rake angles on traversing tools

supported, the breadth of the cutting surface in action is a disadvantage, and liable to accentuate any tendency to chatter or dig in. To reduce this, the tool may be tapered down to a narrow point, with a small radius at the tip.

When round-nosed tools are used for deep traversing cuts towards the left, the main cutting thrust is at an angle to the work axis, as shown in Fig. 6–8. To cut with maximum efficiency under these conditions, therefore, the tool should not only have top rake, but also side rake, as indicated in Fig. 6–9. For light finishing cuts on straight cylindrical work, a tool with a very broad and

FIG. 6–10 Recommended cutting angles for parting tools

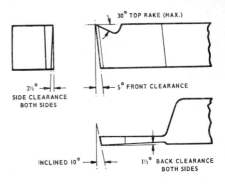

30° TOP RAKE (MAX.)

2½° SIDE CLEARANCE BOTH SIDES

5° FRONT CLEARANCE

INCLINED 10°

1½° BACK CLEARANCE BOTH SIDES

only slightly curved front edge may be used, with coarse traversing feed, but this form of tool may not be found satisfactory on light lathes, in which the tool post and slides may be capable of deflection.

In modern practice, parting-off is generally done by using blades of taper section, mounted in holders either horizontally, or at an angle to provide top take. These simplify grinding and setting, but sometimes lack side rigidity, and may cut out of square. As they have no back clearance, they may tend to jam in a deep cut. If parting tools are forged or ground from solid steel, they will be found to cut most efficiently if ground as shown in Fig. 6–10. The side and back clearance must be kept very small if the tool is made with the minimum width, to avoid wastage of material. In order to part the work piece off clean, with little or no "pip" left in the centre, the front edge is ground at an angle of about 10 degrees. While top rake is generally desirable, it results in lowering the height of the cutting edge each time the front face is reground, until it becomes too low for proper setting. For this reason, some turners prefer to use tools with little or no top rake, unless they can be used in inclined holders. Grooving tools can be made similar in shape to parting tools, except for the front face, which may be dead square, or rounded off, as the operation requires.

The basic shapes of tools shown in the diagrams are all designed for use on steel, but require only alteration of rake angles in order to suit them to other metals. The shapes of tool points may have to be modified to suit particular operations, but subject to this, they cover most requirements for external work.

Form Tools

These can only be used to a limited extent in general workshop practice, as the special tools required are only justified when parts are required in quantity. Such operations as forming V-grooves in pulleys, or concave grooves in terminal heads, can be carried out by slightly modified point or round-nosed tools, but if the cuts are of substantial depth, direct plunge feed imposes abnormal load on both the tool and the work, and it

FIG. 6–11 Holders for parting tool blades by Jones & Shipman Ltd.

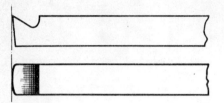

FIG. 6–12: Cambered tool for light finishing

is best to take side cuts as the depth increases, except in the final stages.

Small form tools for semicircular beadings, etc., can be made by drilling holes of the required diameter in carbon steel gauge plate and cutting off across the centre of the hole. After backing off, hardening and tempering, these tools are clamped in a holder, preferably with support on the underside close to the cutting edge. When form tools of elaborate shape need to be made, they may with advantage be of circular form, turned to the required shape from annealed tool steel, and notched to provide the cutting edge. They are clamped to the holder by a centre bolt, in the same way as circular screwcutting tools and chasers.

Chip Breakers

Tools with a groove ground across the top face of the cutting edge are extensively used in industry for heavy machining of tough steel. The main object is to turn the chip sharply and thereby break or shorten it, so that the swarf is easier to dispose of than when it comes off in long coils. It is generally necessary to use a cutter grinder to form the groove, using a formed wheel or one with a radius on the corner. One disadvantage of the chip breaker tool is that regrinding is more

difficult than with normal tools, and soon destroys its usefulness. It is however, possible to obtain much the same effect of breaking the chip by clamping a strip of steel with a bevelled end on top of the tool, fairly close to the cutting edge, to act in a similar manner to the "back iron" of a woodworking plane.

Spring tools were once popular for producing a high finish on steel, particularly where large fillets or internal curves were involved. They are rarely seen in modern practice, as other and more efficient methods, such as contour grinding, are available, but they may be found useful in workshops with limited equipment. The usual form of spring tool is of the inverted swan-neck type, forged or machined from carbon steel, and for maximum efficiency and working life, it may with advantage have a brazed-on tip of high speed steel or tungsten carbide.

A tool with a slightly cambered, wide cutting face is userful for producing a very high finish on steel and may with advantage be used in a spring holder. Fig. 6–12.

Adhesion of Metal to Tool point

In some machining operations, metal is liable to adhere to the tool point and cause it to cut roughly with increased load. With some of the ductile metals such as soft aluminium alloys, it is difficult to eliminate this tendency, but it can be mitigated by the use of a suitable lubricant, and by reducing the depth of cut or the traversing feed. Increase of rake angle is sometimes helpful. Usually the metal adhesion does not harm the edge of the tool, and it can be removed with the aid of a honing slip; it is sometimes stated that it actually protects the edge during heavy machining.

Negative Rake

The main object of using tools with obtuse included cutting angles, or in other words, negative rake, is to strengthen the tool point against extremely heavy loading, and to provide the utmost rigidity. Such angles are most appropriate to production work, with tools tipped with tungsten carbide or ultra-hard metal, which is liable to fracture unless adequately supported. The application of negative rake tools to general-purpose lathes is limited, as they absorb considerable power and are less adaptable than the usual forms of tools. It has been mentioned that one of the objects of *positive* top rake is to enable the tool to penetrate the work with the minimum driving effort, and it should be used to advantage on steel and other appropriate materials.

Tool Post Design

Various kinds of fixtures are used for mounting tools on the slide rest of a lathe. The term "tool post" is somewhat archaic, and was originally applied to primitive bolting-down or clamping devices, but it is still used to define modern, and often elaborate fixtures, which carry lathe tools either directly or in subsidiary holders. Most improvements in tool post design have been intended to give greater facility for the adjustment of the tool, especially in respect of height, but some of them have achieved this only at the cost of rigidity. There is still much to be said in favour of simple fixtures which support the tool as directly and securely as possible.

The basic requirements of the tool post, and the forces which it is required to withstand, are shown in Fig. 6–13, which represents a type which has been used on several simple lathes. It consists of a short pillar with a spigot (not shown) which fits a socket in the slide rest and can be clamped in any position of rotation by a set screw or wedge bolt. Either an open or closed slot is provided to accommodate the tool, which is set to centre height by the use of one or more packing slips of suitable thickness, and clamped in position by a single set screw.

When the tool is in normal use, the cutting torque tends to deflect the tool downwards, and assuming that it does not bend, this force is transmitted to the tool post as shown in the elevation view. Under the load imposed in traversing or facing operations, there is also a force tending to slew the tool around in the opposite direction to the feed movement. Should any deflection take place, digging-in or "hogging" of the tool point will occur, and in extreme cases, the tool point may be broken or the work spoilt. The importance of rigidity in the tool post, and in the method of fixing the tool, is clearly demonstrated; and it is equally obvious that tools should

FIG. 6–13: Forces exerted on cutting tools

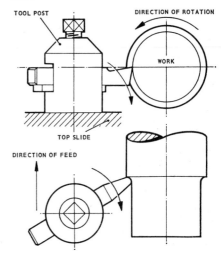

FIG. 6–17: Myford quick-setting tool with convex packing block or "boat"

FIG. 6–14: Open clamp type of tool post as used on Myford ML7 and Super 7 lathes

FIG. 6–16: Lantern type tool post on Boxford lathe

FIG. 6–15: Block type tool post for Colchester lathes (optional)

FIG. 6–18: Four-way turret tool post on Colchester lathe

never project from the tool post farther than is necessary or than the operation requires.

Many tool posts now employed have a central stud or pillar mounted on the top slide. The simplest form of these has a plate, roughly triangular in shape, which clamps the tool by its broad edge when pulled down by the nut on the single stud. To support the apex of the plate, a jack screw is provided, adjustable to suit the thickness of the tool and its packing, so that the plate is more or less horizontal. In the improved form of this fixture used on Myford ML 7 and Super 7 lathes, the plate is a casting of specially rigid section, and the thrust washer is spherically curved on the underside to fit a seating of similar shape. The jack screw, which is knurled for easy adjustment, has also a spherically seated base pad. These refinements enable the clamp to hold the tool firmly even when the height adjustment is not perfect, and provide the utmost latitude for holding a wide range of tool shapes and sizes. Fig. 6–14.

Either openside or closed slot tool posts are used on several types of lathes. The type shown in Fig. 6–15 is held down on the slide rest by a single stud so as to be capable of rotation, but the tool is clamped in the slot by two or more extra set screws. While the security of this type of fixture is generally satisfactory, it calls for two stages of adjustment, and for using a tool of specified size, requires more clearance over the level of the slide rest.

The enclosed "box" tool holder used for several years on Drummond and Myford M type lathes employed a central pillar of large diameter, on which the tool clamp is mounted so as to be capable of rotation and height adjustment, and secured in position by a split clamp. A square slot is provided to take the tool, which is secured by set screws. In an improved version of this device, a screw is provided to adjust the height of the tool. This is a very facile device, but its rigidity is somewhat inferior to fixtures which clamp the tool down firmly to the slide surface, and the size and shape of tool which can be used in it is limited.

The "lantern" (Fig. 6–16) tool post, commonly known as the American type, though it has been used for many years on British and Continental lathes as well, gives the greatest facility for setting the tool to correct height, and clamping it in

any position of rotation by means of a single set screw. Its essential features are the use of a convex-based rocker, seated on the concave face of a loose bush, and a circular pillar, shaped at the base to fit a T-slot in the slide rest, and having a vertical slot to take the tool. By shifting the rocker forward or back on its seating, the tool is tilted so that the height of its edge can be adjusted; it is then clamped in position by the central set screw. A somewhat modified form of lantern tool post, mostly used on light instrument lathes, employs a screwed sleeve to adjust height instead of the rocker, so that the tool is kept horizontal.

Tilting adjustment of the tool is often objected to because it alters the rake and clearance angles, but in view of the small amount of movement necessary, this is not usually a very serious matter. A more practical objection is that the lantern tool post will only accommodate a relatively narrow tool; it is best suited to take the deep section holders for small tool bits. The rigidity of this tool post is inferior to that of some other types, but it is generally firm enough to cope with moderate duties, and its handiness largely compensates any short-comings in this respect. The rocker principle of height adjustment has been applied to several forms of tool posts, and also holders which can be used in plate or other fixtures.

The Myford quick-setting lathe tools have concave recesses on the underside of their shanks, and are seated on a centrally grooved convex packing block or "boat", on which they can be rocked to adjust the height of the cutting edge. These tools are made in a full range of shapes, with high speed steel tips welded to carbon steel shanks, either $\frac{3}{8}$ in. or $\frac{1}{2}$ in. square. Fig. 6–17.

Many lathes are equipped with a four-way "turret" tool post, either as a standard or alternative item of equipment. This is usually made to fit, and be secured to the slide by, the central stud, and may be made to rotate into any position, or to index to a limited number of stations, four or eight, for instance. This is helpful for approximate sizing of work, but limits adaptability to some extent. The ability to keep four tools set up

FIG. 6–19: Colchester quick-setting tool post

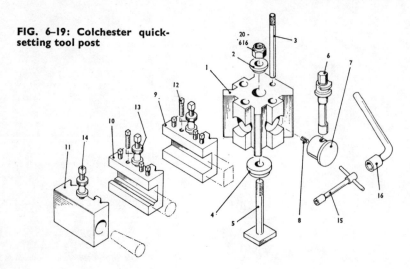

for work, and to bring them into action instantly, is a great advantage when tools of various shapes need to be used on a single workpiece. Tools for roughing and finishing, chamfering and parting off, may all be needed on a relatively simple machined component. Fig. 6–18.

It is, however, important when using any multi-tool fixture, that the tools do not get in each other's way, or project in such a way that they may get caught in the operator's clothing, or cause injury to hands. This may be prevented by the use of a tool post fitted at the rear of the cross slide, with the tools inverted. Most rear tool posts are equipped with means of holding only one tool, usually for parting or chamfering, but there is no reason why they could not be provided with two or more tool stations, which would extend their usefulness.

FIG. 6–20: Myford rear tool post in use on a heavy parting-off operation

The quick-change tool post used on Colchester lathes employs a main block (1) which can be mounted on any lathe of suitable size, having a flat surface on the top slide, with a central stud or a slot for a vertical T-bolt (5). Seatings on one or more sides of the block are machined to fit the detachable tool holders (9, 10 and 11) which are positively located by V-grooves which engage the corners of the block. Vertical T-slots in each of the holders engage a clamp pad with a T-head (7), fitted to a recess in the block, and normally pushed outwards by a small spring (8). When either holder is fitted to the block and engaged with the clamp pad, it can be secured firmly in position by the action of the eccentric bolt (6).

Height adjustment of the tool-holders is obtained by means of screws (14) having a collar which engages a groove in the external part of the clamping bolt (6). The three holders shown are suitable for holding square, round, or taper-shanked tools, the former two being clamped by square headed set screws (12). Adjustment for tool height must of course be carried out before tightening the clamp bolt (6). A dowel pin (3) is provided for locating the block in one, or any required number of pre-set angular positions. It will be noted that neither the angle nor the lateral position of the tool point is varied in adjusting or changing the holder. Fig. 6–19.

Rear Tool Posts

Some of the subsidiary operations in lathe work, such as parting-off or chamfering, can most conveniently be carried out by the use of a tool mounted at the back of the cross slide. For running the lathe in the normal direction, the tool must be inverted, and mounted higher than usual, to bring its cutting edge to centre height. Inverted tools are not favoured for major lathe operations, as it is preferable to be able to see the edge of the tool in action, but this is not so important where tools do not need to be closely watched. In most cases a parting tool will be found to work more smoothly in the inverted position, as the direction of load on the complete tool assembly tends to relieve stress rather than to cause digging in. Fig. 6–20.

The rear tool post specially made for Myford lathes, but adaptable to other lathes of similar centre height, is fitted with a rocking pad for height adjustment of the tool and is secured to the cross slide by a single T-bolt. Detachable tool heads to take two or more tools, and capable of indexing them in position as required, can be fitted to specially made tool posts, but these are not available ready made. They may also carry boring, threading or other tools, and undoubtedly save a great deal of time in avoiding the need for changing the front tools. A cross slide of adequate length is necessary to carry a rear tool post without cramping or reducing the latitude of slide movements. These and other auxiliary tool fixtures all play a part in extending the versatility of relatively simple lathes; they also emphasise the advantage of flat cross slides on which they can be readily mounted.

CHAPTER 7

TURNING BETWEEN CENTRES

IN order to mount shafts or other work pieces for turning between centres, both ends must be drilled or indented to locate and support the pieces concentrically. Several methods of finding the centre of the work piece are employed. It may be laid in a pair of V-blocks on the marking-off table, and cross lines scribed on the end faces with the aid of a surface gauge. By rotating the piece into three or more positions, and adjusting the height of the scriber by trial, the centre can be located within close limits, prior to centre-punching and drilling. Where it is not convenient to mark out work in this way, there are simple centre-finding appliances available, such as that shown in Fig. 7–1, or a centre-punch with a conical guide, commonly known as a "bell" centre-punch, can be applied. These devices are described in the handbook

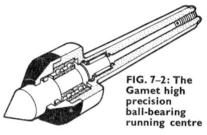

FIG. 7–2: The Gamet high precision ball-bearing running centre

Lathe Accessories. If the work piece is not too long, and can be held temporarily in a chuck to run as truly as possible, it can be drilled directly from the tailstock; or the drill may be mounted in the live mandrel socket and the work, centred in a steady, presented to it by feeding from the tailstock end.

The indentations in the ends in the bar should be drilled to the same angle as the lathe centres (usually 60 degrees inclusive) with a relieved centre to avoid fouling the point of the centres. The smoothness and circular accuracy of the drilled centres are also important, as they have an influence on the quality of the turned work. The most suitable tool for producing the indentations is the combined drill and counter-sink, known as a centre-drill. It is relatively inexpensive, and can be obtained in a range of sizes for use in the lathe, drilling machine or hand drill. Where there are no restrictions on the depth of the indentations, they should be drilled sufficiently deep to provide adequate support

FIG. 7–1: Marking the centre with the aid of the Moore & Wright centre-square

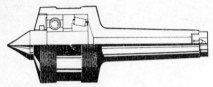

FIG. 7–3: Section of the Archer ball and taper roller bearing centre by Frank Guylee Ltd.

and wearing property, but sometimes the nature of the work makes it necessary to keep them small and shallow, in which case the accuracy of drilling is still more important. For work which already has a hole in the centre, the mouth of the hole may be chamfered or countersunk at the required angle; in the case of tapped holes, the chamfering must be carried well beyond the outer diameter of the thread, so that this does not influence its accuracy. A large centre-drill, or a specially made cutter, may be used for this operation; a "cutting-centre" is provided for this purpose on some lathes, and may also be used for truing up indentations which have become worn or otherwise roughened.

Before mounting work between the lathe centres, care should be taken to see that they are properly fitted to their sockets, and are smooth and true on their projecting points. Dirt and swarf should be scrupulously excluded from the sockets; scored surfaces which may occur in the sockets, or on the shanks of the centres, are fatal to accuracy and must be smoothed off or otherwise corrected. Obviously there is a limit to the number of times this can be done before the fit of the centres is permanently impaired, and for this reason the need for it should be avoided by every possible means. In the normal use of lathe centres, there should be no reason for them to slip in the sockets and cause scoring, but sometimes other tools are fitted to the sockets,

such as cutters or screw threading tools, which involve considerable torque, and are liable to be the worst offenders in causing damage to the sockets. A felt plug, mounted on a twisted wire in the manner of a bottle brush, is a handy device for cleaning lathe sockets, and may also be used to apply a trace of light oil to prevent jamming or seizure of the centres.

The "live" or headstock centre must be fitted to run truly within the closest possible limits, because any concentric error will be transmitted to the finished work. It need not be dead hard, because there is little relative movement between it and the work. Should it become inaccurate, it can be machined true while fitted to the socket, but this treatment should be necessary only very infrequently. Otherwise it indicates that the headstock socket is out of truth, or that the centre does not fit properly for some reason, and appropriate action should be taken to correct either fault.

The "dead" or tailstock centre needs to be hard in order to withstand the wear as the work revolves on it. So long as it is smooth and truly conical on the point, its concentricity is important only in so far as it affects alignment with the live centre, and thus the parallel accuracy of the work. In some lathes which have no means of adjusting the crosswise position of the complete tailstock, an eccentric centre has been used to correct error in this respect; or the centre point has been mounted on a short slide to provide more positive set-over adjustment. In addition to point centres, it is often necessary to provide other forms of centres which have already been described under the heading of accessories. With the increasingly heavy duty required in modern lathe practice, the tail centre is subject to considerable wear, and several kinds of anti-friction centres, having the point mounted in running bearings, are extensively employed. The simplest of these is one having a floating head, taking its end thrust against a hardened steel ball seated in the shank. Being enclosed, this can be kept well lubricated and free from dirt, so that it reduces friction and avoids wear of the actual conical point.

Running Centres

For more continuous or heavier duty, running centres with ball and roller bearings are employed. These are of various forms, including the Gamet type, which employs opposed angular contact ball races to take axial and radial loads, with a needle roller guide bearing at the inner end, and the Archer, which has taper toller bearings in combination with ball races. The Lunzer rotating centres are of various types, some of which have two widely spaced radial bearings with a heavy duty double ball thrust bearing between them. In all cases these centres have standard taper shanks, and are totally enclosed and sealed, with provision for lubrication in the form of oil or grease nipples. Besides having normal centre points, they are also made with large diameter cones to suit hollow work, or with female or reduced diameter points, or adaptors to take pressed-on cones of any size or angle required. In all rotating centres, it is most important that the point or core should be concentric with its bearings within very close limits, and should remain so under the heaviest working conditions. Figs 7–2, 3.

Methods of Driving Work

Carriers of various kinds, clamped to the driving end of the workpiece, and having a projecting arm to

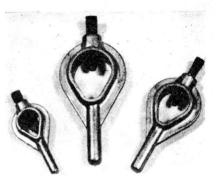

FIG. 7–4: Three sizes of carriers by Myfords Ltd.

engage the driving pin or slot of the catchplate, are usually employed to transmit the drive from the live headstock. The space occupied by the carrier limits the traverse of the tool, so that it is not possible to machine the full length of work when driven in this way. But when the accessible length has been dealt with, the work may be turned end for end and the carrier clamped to the part already machined. If the live centre runs truly, concentric accuracy will be maintained, and one of the great advantages of between-centres turning is that the work can be removed and replaced as many times as may be necessary for fitting or "offering up" the work to a mating part. It is also possible, when skimming up a

FIG. 7–5: An arm bolted to the work, serving as a substitute for a carrier

FIG. 7–6: Machining edges of marine type bearings on connecting rod assembly

worn journal, to ensure that it runs truly if the original drilled centres are in good condition.

When clamping a carrier to work which has been turned to finished size, precautions must be taken to avoid bruising the surface by the point of the clamping screw. A pad of soft metal such as aluminium or copper may be interposed between the screw and the work, but often it is better to make a loose split bush, which gives more positive protection at all points of contact. Sometimes it may be more convenient to avoid the need for using a carrier on finished work, by fastening a projecting arm to the work in other ways. In turning a connecting rod which has a flanged foot, for instance, the bolt-holes in the foot may be used to hold the arm, so that the full length of the taper shank may be machined in one operation. Rods of the marine type often have the crankhead brasses machined over the ends to match the contour of the flanged foot. In this case the outer end is centre-drilled, and the work is driven by means of a bolt through the cross hole at the small end of the rod. Figs. 7–5, 6.

Whatever form of radial projection is employed, it is most important that it should engage the driving pin squarely, and not impose any wedg-

ing action which might possibly cause side thrust on the live centre; also that no part of the arm should foul the centre. When the nature of the work involves intermittent cutting, such as in turning off the corners of a square or rectangular shaft, there is a tendency for the carrier to move away from the driving pin between cuts. This not only causes undesirable noise, but the shock of engagement is bad for the lathe centres and possibly other parts. To avoid the backlash, the carrier is sometimes tied or wired to the driving pin, but a better method is to use a forked carrier with a set screw to take up the clearance on the driving pin, or some equivalent device.

A simple example of between-centres turning is shown in Fig. 7–7, where a short shaft, centre-drilled at both ends, is mounted between the lathe centres. At the left-hand end, a carrier is fitted, with its tail end in contact with the driving pin of the catchplate. About half the length of the shaft is being turned down to a smaller diameter, by means of a right-hand side tool. The object of this illustration is to demonstrate basic principles of this particular method. Before starting the machining operation, the distance from the end of the work to the shoulder may be marked off, using the point of the tool, and allowing a small amount for finishing after turning to the required size. If the end faces of the shaft have not already been machined, a cutaway-centre may be fitted to the tailstock so that they can be faced with the side tool, and if necessary, the total length of the shaft adjusted while between centres. If a square shoulder is required, a side tool with a sharp-cornered cutting edge must be used, but unless this is absolutely

FIG. 7–7: Work mounted between centres on Colchester lathe

FIG. 7–9: Machining a pair of round-headed bolts by back-to-back methods

essential, it is better to use a tool with a round nose, or one having a radius honed on the tip, to produce an internal radius, or fillet, on the work. This is particularly important for work that is liable to be highly stressed when in use. Sharp internal corners are a potential source of weakness, and may possibly become a focus for cracks in time.

Where a considerable amount of metal needs to be machined away, the work may be roughed down to near-finished size by means of a "ripping" tool with cutting angles designed for this kind of operation, prior to turning to exact size and shape with a keen finishing tool. For making small headed shafts or bolts in pairs or batches, it is often convenient to start with pieces twice the full length required, plus cutting-off allowance, and centred at both ends. Material of hexagonal or other appropriate shape may be used to produce the head without need for subsequent machining. Fig. 7–9. After turning one end to length and diameter required, and threading or screwcutting where called for, the

work is reversed end for end and the process repeated. To avoid damage to finished threads, a split nut may be clamped to them by the carrier screw. The pieces may be divided in the

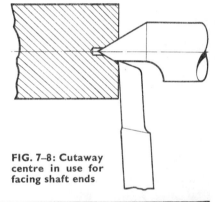

FIG. 7–8: Cutaway centre in use for facing shaft ends

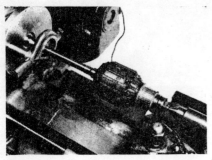

FIG. 7–10: Truing up an electric motor commutator between centres

middle, either by sawing, or parting-off, and facing in the lathe chuck.

An operation which is often encountered in the jobbing machine shop is the truing up of a motor commutator, such as shown in Fig. 7–10. Provided that the shaft was originally made with truly drilled centres, and that these are free from burrs or other damage, it may conveniently be mounted between centres; but just in case it may have become bent or distorted in use, a check should be made on the journal surfaces immediately adjacent to the armature, to see that they run truly when thus mounted. If not, they should be corrected by straightening the shaft—a rather delicate operation which is best carried out under a press, with the shaft mounted in V-blocks. For the particular operation shown, only very light cuts can be taken to true the commutator surface, and it is in order to mount the assembly in this way, but in view of the slenderness of the shaft, it is often an advantage to hold it in a true-running collet chuck, as close to the armature as possible.

Crankshaft Turning

A convenient way of machining the main and crankpin journals of crankshafts is by mounting them between centres on the respective axes. In a typical case a single-throw crankshaft is made from flat bar material, which is first marked out accurately to the shape required, and the centre lines produced on the end faces. It is most important that the centre lines should be exactly parallel with each other, and also in alignment on the end faces. The intersection of the lines is carefully centre-punched, and centre drilled to sufficient size and depth for ample support. In the sequence of operations shown in Fig. 7/11, a third centre is drilled midway between the other two, in order to mount the piece for turning the edges of the webs, but this is not necessary if they are to be finished with square edges.

The first operation in this case is to mount the bar by the middle centre and machine the webs as shown. As a carrier cannot readily be fitted to the work, it is clamped to the driving pin in such a position that the tail engages the side of the bar. It is now necessary to cut away some of the unwanted material adjacent to the crankpin, to reduce the amount of metal which must be removed by turning operations. This can best be done by sawing down inside the lines which denote the inner sides of the webs, and drilling holes near the crankpin line, as closely spaced as possible, so that the surplus metal can be broken out. (It is assumed that no machine tool facilities are available for these operations).

The work is now mounted on the crankpin centres for turning the journal; a tool having sufficient length of cutting edge to reach down into the gap will be required. It is not generally advisable, at least on a light lathe, to use a tool wide enough to form the crankpin and the sides of the web in a single plunge cut. A narrower tool, which allows of traversing sideways on the journal with light cuts, is to be recommended,

FIG. 7–11:
Sequence of
operations in
machining a
single-throw
crankshaft
between centres

FIG. 7–12: Turning a four-throw crank-shaft between centres

but it should be of sufficient depth to provide rigidity, and should have side clearance on both sides, so that it can be used to face the inner sides of the webs. The front corners of the cutting edge should be rounded slightly to form fillets in the corners of the journal.

When all necessary work on the crankpin is completed—not before—the surplus metal adjacent to the main journal can be cut away by sawing or other methods. It is a sound policy to retain solid metal where possible, in order to provide rigidity, until its removal becomes necessary. A crankshaft is not a very rigid component unless the journals are made abnormally large in relation to their throw radius. When mounted on the main journal centres, there is a wedging action which tends to spring the webs inwards under the cutting pressure of the tool. For this reason, a temporary gap piece should be made to a close fit between the webs, and clamped in position by any convenient means while the main journals are being turned. In this case, a bolt and two washers are used to hold the gap piece.

Multiple-throw cranks present more difficult machining problems, but when made from flat bar material, with throws at 180 degrees, the same methods of setting out and centre-drilling the end faces can be employed. As the partially machined

shaft is very liable to deflection, it is necessary to proceed very cautiously with the turning operations, especially on the centre crankpins. The side projections of the end pieces in which the crankpin centres are drilled must of course be cut away before machining the main journals. A suitable long-reach tool for turning the crankpins may be made from a piece of deep section high-speed steel, such as a parting-tool blade, but it must be rigidly held in a closely fitted holder to avoid side deflection in use. Fig. 7–12.

Forged crankshafts, or other semi-finished types which are not provided with a "tail" or other projection in which throw centres can be drilled, need to have a temporary throw piece fitted on each end. This must be very securely fitted, so that it cannot shift while turning the crankpins. Various methods of fixing, including set screws or split clamps, are employed for this purpose, but in all cases, the throw centres must be in exact alignment on both ends. For multiple cranks at angles other than 180 degrees—such as three-throw cranks at 120 degrees—the throw pieces may be in the form of discs on which the full set of throw centres are set out to close limits, by indexing with the aid of a dividing head or a sine bar if available. In steam engines, it is common to machine the eccentric sheaves from solid, and their throw centres are also set out in a similar manner.

There are several other ways of machining crankshafts, depending largely on individual design. In modern crankshaft production, special chucking machines are used, in which the webs are held close up to the crankpins to be machined, thereby providing maximum rigidity.

Overhung crankshafts are often most conveniently machined in eccentric turning fixtures, mounted on the lathe faceplate. But in all methods, the principle of ensuring that the main and crankpin journals are exactly parallel to each other, and at the correct radius, must be strictly observed.

Offset Centre Turning

For most between-centre operations, the live and tailstock centres must be aligned more or less accurately with each other, so that the tool, traversed by the saddle motion, produces a parallel cut. Error in this respect will result in turning taper to a greater or less degree. Misalignment of centres may be caused by initial faults in the lathe construction, or slackness in the tailstock guide or barrel fitting. When a lathe is well worn, the action of clamping these movements may result in throwing the centres out of line. But even when their alignment is exact, it is possible that the saddle movement may not be truly parallel with the lathe axis. While these faults are unlikely to be found in good quality lathes, their potential existence should always be recognised, and steps taken to avoid them. Some means of adjusting the alignment of the tail centre may be regarded as essential for accurate work.

Deliberate offsetting of the tail centres is commonly employed as a means of turning tapers of greater length than can conveniently be dealt with by the swivelling top slide. For this purpose, most lathes are provided with means of adjusting the tailstock crosswise, to offset the centre to a certain distance in one or both directions. The amount of taper produced in this way depends on the length of work between centres in conjunction with the offset distance.

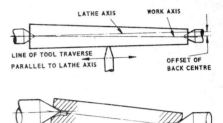

FIG. 7–13: Taper turning by means of offset centres

For instance, a length of 12 in., and an offset of $\frac{5}{16}$ in., produces a taper of $\frac{5}{8}$ in. per foot, or an *included* angle of very slightly under 3 degrees (2 degrees, 59 minutes 4 seconds to be exact). For slight tapers of this order, the method produces fairly accurate results, but with an increase of offset, errors are liable to be introduced, because the centre-drilled holes in the ends of the work do not seat truly on the points of the lathe centres. This effect is seen in exaggerated form in Fig. 7–13.

It is of course possible to calculate the angle of taper in any particular instance by trigonometrical methods, when using offset turning, but in view of the imperfect bearing contact of the centres, the question arises regarding the exact point from which the *length* of the shaft should be measured. Theoretically, it should be midway in the conical part of the centre-drilled holes, but this is often difficult to locate accurately. When it is necessary to machine a number of parts to a uniform taper, some form of length gauge with points to locate in the centre-drilled holes should be used to ensure equality in their effective lengths.

The only type of centre which would provide a remedy for imperfect bearing of the work centres when turning tapers is one having a spherical tip, but this is not a standard

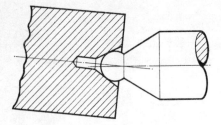

FIG. 7–14: Spherical-tipped centre in use for taper turning

accessory, and would have to be specially made. Sometimes the centres in the work are drilled with a somewhat more obtuse-angled countersinking cutter, so that they bear only at the small end, and minimise the error to some extent. Generally speaking, however, parts taper turned between centres are of such a nature that critical angle of taper is not necessary. Such items as engine columns, connecting and eccentric rods, etc., allow some latitude in this respect, so long as they look right.

The most convenient and accurate appliance for this work is a taper turning attachment, which is usually fitted to the back of the lathe bed, and comprises a slide which can be adjusted within certain angular limits. The cross slide of the lathe is disconnected from its feed screw and

engaged with the angular slide. To obtain cross movement for in-feeding of the tool, the swivelling top slide can be set at right angles to the lathe axis, or at some intermediate angle. The advantage of such attachments is that they can be used on any workpieces, either mounted between centres, on the faceplate, or in the chuck, and when once set, produce exactly the same angle of taper, irrespective of the length of the workpiece. Fig. 7–15.

Special Work Driving Appliances

The use of ordinary carriers for driving the work is sometimes objected to, mostly on the grounds of safety. There is a risk that the carrier may catch in the sleeve of the operator, and cause personal injury; it may also catch up coils of swarf and wind them around the work, or throw them in all directions. Various driving appliances are used which eliminate the need for clamping screws and other projections, and also speed up the loading and unloading of the work. The Pratt patent work driver has three internal gripping jaws in the form of eccentrically pivoted discs, having teeth on their outer edges, shaped so that they grip the work in the direction of rotation. Increase in the cutting torque automatically tightens the grip of the jaws, but they are easily released by rotating the driver in the reverse direction. The driver may have a dog or other projection on the back to engage either a pin or a slot in the catchplate; or it can be fitted to the mandrel nose like a chuck and the catchplate thus eliminated. As the gripping jaws leave their "footprints" on the work, this driver should not be used on finished

FIG. 7–15: Taper turning attachment fitted to Myford ML7 lathe

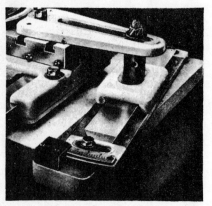

FIG. 7–17: The Giromat end face driving device

surfaces where marks would be objectionable. Fig. 7–16.

The Giromat driving device operates by engaging the end face of the workpiece by means of a hardened face ratchet on the outside of a live centre in the rotating body. Movement of the ratchet is controlled by a face cam on the rear of its flange, so that the grip in this case also is proportional to the torque. This device has the advantage that it enables machining to be carried out to the full length of the work,

FIG. 7–16: The Pratt patent work driver

provided that the finished size is not smaller than the outside diameter of the ratchet. As the ends of shafts or other workpieces are not normally used as working surfaces, the marks made by the gripping teeth are not objected to as a rule. The end thrust produced by this device, however, makes it desirable to use it in conjunction with a running centre in the tailstock, to resist the endwise load and avoid excessive friction. Fig. 7–17.

Location from Bore

Workpieces which have already been bored concentrically may be set on a mandrel between centres for further operations on their external surfaces. Standard mandrels, in a wide range of sizes, are obtainable; they are usually made with a slight taper throughout their length, hardened and precision ground. Their use is obviously confined to work bored to a press fit on them, but it is practicable to make special mandrels to fit bores of any size. These need not be hardened if care is taken to keep the surface, and particularly the drilled centres, in good condition. True running of the mandrel is

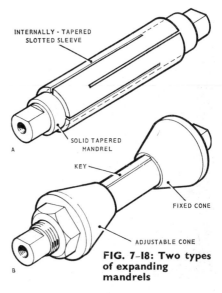

INTERNALLY - TAPERED
SLOTTED SLEEVE

SOLID TAPERED
MANDREL

KEY

FIXED CONE

ADJUSTABLE CONE

A

B

FIG. 7–18: Two types of expanding mandrels

obviously essential for precision work, but subject to this condition, location from a pre-machined bore is often the best way of dealing with work which cannot be machined on all required surfaces at one operation.

Expanding mandrels of various kinds are used for mounting work in which the diameter of the bore cannot be guaranteed accurate. The mandrel shown in Fig. 7–18(A), is turned to a taper of 3 to 5 degrees inclusive, and a sleeve with a matching internal taper, turned parallel on the outside, is fitted to it. About four slots, extending for three-quarters of its length, are cut from each end of the sleeve, so that it is capable of being expanded when moved along the tapered mandrel. This will fit bores within a latitude of 0·010 in. per inch diameter, and spare sleeves to fit various bore sizes may be provided if required.

The mandrel shown at B has a wider latitude of size adjustment, but limited area of gripping surface, and it is best suited to pipe work in which it is possible to chamfer both ends of

the bore to correspond with the angle of the cones. It is advisable to turn the fixed cone from the solid, and to make the other cone a close sliding fit on the parallel part of the mandrel. A key should be fitted to prevent rotation of the adjustable cone, which may with advantage be taper turned in position. Suitable taper angles for the cones are from 20 to 30 degrees inclusive. The threaded end of the mandrel should be screwcut to provide the maximum accuracy, and the thrust face of the nut machined truly square with the thread.

In fitting work to plain mandrels, a press of some kind should be used in preference to hammering, which is liable to cause damage by burring up centre holes or "mushrooming" the outer faces in course of time. For light operations, it is often sufficient to wring the work on the mandrel by hand. In any case, no greater force should be used for mounting the work than is necessary to hold it securely against cutting torque. But slipping of the work on the mandrel must be avoided, as it may cause scoring or even seizure, thereby destroying an accurate and highly finished bore. Though lubri-

FIG. 7–19: A steam engine cylinder mounted on a stub mandrel for machining end face

FIG. 7-20: A flywheel secured to a stub mandrel by an end nut for external machining

cating a mandrel tends to reduce the grip of the work, it is sometimes a prudent policy to apply a smear of "moly" grease, so that if slip takes place, it is not liable to do much harm.

As an alternative to mounting mandrels between centres, it is sometimes more convenient to use stub or pin mandrels held in the chuck as shown in Fig. 7–19, and with or without additional tailstock support. Such mandrels are usually turned in position to fit the particular job, but if it becomes necessary to re-fit them after removal, they should be checked for concentric accuracy before again being used. If more than one component needs to be machined at one setting of the stub mandrel, some means of removing it without disturbing the mandrel may need to be provided. Sometimes it may be convenient to ease the fit of the mandrel and provide it with a clamping nut on the end, as in the example shown in Fig. 7–20. Either parallel or taper-bored components may be mounted in this way for final machining of external surfaces. Work which must, on account of its size, or for heavy machining, be held on a faceplate for adequate support, can be located from bore by means of a stub mandrel fitted to the headstock mandrel socket, but care must be taken to see that it is not forced out of truth when the clamps are tightened.

Eccentric location from bore is practicable by the use of an offset stub mandrel, but at all costs the work must be prevented from slipping, as any shift during the machining operation would destroy the work, and possibly the tool as well.

CHAPTER 8

CHUCK AND FACEPLATE WORK

THE facility with which work can be held in modern lathe chucks has led to many changes in turning methods in recent years. Much of the work which was formerly machined between centres, or by location from bore on a mandrel, is now dealt with more efficiently and expeditiously when mounted in a three-jaw or four-jaw chuck. For round or hexagonal bar stock up to a moderate size limit, the three-jaw self-centring chuck is generally most convenient, provided that the work does not overhang too far in relation to the length which can be gripped in the chuck jaws.

Bars of small enough diameter to pass through the hollow mandrel can be dealt with in lengths, which may even extend well beyond the tail end of the mandrel, though in extreme cases some steadying support to prevent "skipping-roping" may be necessary. If the workpieces are short, it is often convenient to turn them from bars of greater length and part them off when finished, rather than cutting them to near-finished length beforehand. The waste of metal entailed in parting off can be tolerated, if it simplifies holding the work and avoiding the need for a second operation. This applies particularly to the use of collet chucks, which also, as already explained, will hold stock bars of accurate graded size more truly than the average three-jaw chuck, and without marking finished surfaces.

Wherever the surface of the work is imperfect either in finish or roundness, it is not advisable to hold it in a self-centring chuck. While it would not do much harm to hold a round casting in the chuck for a very light operation such as facing or centre-drilling, the surface is often so far out of round, due to the presence of "flashes" or other moulding inaccuracies, that its concentric truth could not be relied upon. It is better to mount such work in the four-jaw chuck, despite the greater time and care involved in setting up.

A sound rule in all kinds of lathe work is that operations should be planned in such a way that all surfaces which need to be true with each other can be machined at a single setting wherever possible. For

FIG. 8–1: Overhanging work supported by back centre

instance, in machining a spigoted housing or a gland, it is essential that the bore and the spigot should be exactly concentric, and the faces square with the axis. Less important surfaces, such as outer flange faces, may be machined in a second chucking operation, though parting off of the work may produce a positively true and sufficiently well-finished surface. Both in details of component design, and methods of machining, this axiom often seems to be disregarded, with the result that either the finished parts are inaccurate, or elaborate re-setting is necessary to avoid errors.

Where the work projects too far from the chuck for adequate rigidity, it is sound policy to support the outer end by centre-drilling it and advancing the tailstock centre to engage it. The operation shown in Fig. 8–1 illustrates the turning of a bronze bobbin, which will eventually be the barrel of a fabricated steam engine cylinder, supported in this way for all external turning operations prior to parting off; the end has been faced while using a cutaway centre for support. Hollow pieces can be supported by means of a pipe centre, if the mouth of the bore is countersunk or chamfered to an angle of 60 degrees. Alternatively, the piece can be located from bore on a mandrel for external turning.

Many turners now use chuck mounting, in conjunction with the tailstock centre, for practically all projecting parts, even including long and slender shafts. The support which is provided by the grip of the chuck jaws is more rigid than that obtained by its bearing on the live centre, on the same principle as that of a beam having its end "tied" to its column, in comparison with one which is only loosely supported. This applies also to boring bars and mounting mandrels.

In addition to affording a firmer grip than the three-jaw chuck, the four-jaw chuck also has a much greater latitude for holding work of irregular shape, or out of centre. It is also capable of coping more adequately with work projecting some distance from the jaws, though it is still a prudent policy to support the end with the back centre where possible, as shown in the machining of a heavy casting (Fig. 8–2). Setting up castings in the four-jaw chuck is often regarded as a tedious process, and is sometimes shirked, though it is an essential process which cannot be completely eliminated from lathe operation technique. Various aids to setting up are available, including test indicators, which will be described in a later chapter. But for setting up to moderate limits of concentricity, such as required for castings or similar parts which have to be machined on most external surfaces, nothing more elaborate need be used than a piece of chalk or a grease pencil. The crank disc shown in Fig. 8–3 is held in the reversed jaws of the chuck and rotated at medium speed; while the chalk, rubbed down to a blunt point, is presented to it by the hand, steadied by the tool post, and advanced gradually to touch the work surface. This will indicate the high spots, leaving a mark to show which of the jaws should be tightened or loosened to set the work truly.

In the hands of experienced turners, quite high accuracy can be obtained by this and other rough-and-ready methods, including the audible scratch of a scriber point, or the visible proximity of a tool or other projection held in the tool post. Work which has previously been marked out may be set up with the aid of a stationary scriber held adjacent to a marked circle, or a punched centre point. Several devices

---

FIG. 8–3: Approximately true setting by the use of chalk

known generally as "wobblers", are also used for this purpose, and a magnifying lens is often useful as a visual aid. But for the highest precision, the use of a dial test indicator is recommended, Fig. 8–4.

When holding work with non-circular exterior surfaces, it may be found necessary to interpose packing slips between the work and the

FIG. 8–2: Heavy castings, however firmly chucked, may need tailstock support

chuck jaws. In the machining of a steam engine cylinder casting such as that shown in Fig. 8–5, the narrow rim at the back does not afford adequate surface for a good grip, so parallel strips are interposed so that the grip of the jaws is applied equally to both front and back rims. Sometimes it is better to apply short packing slips to bear on the recessed part of the casting, but in either case, care should be taken to avoid crushing or distorting relatively fragile work by excessive tightening of the chuck jaws. When finished work is held in either three-jaw or four-jaw chucks, the surface may be protected by thin slips of aluminium or copper sheet, or by pads of soft metal attached to the jaws in any convenient way.

For workpieces which have part of the outer surface at a much

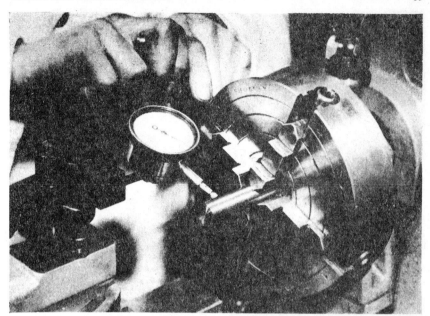

FIG. 8–4: Precision setting with the aid of a dial test indicator

greater radius than the major part to be machined, it may be necessary to reverse one or more of the chuck jaws. The facing and boring of parts such as links and connecting rods with one or more offset centres, as shown in Fig. 8–6 may call for this treatment. When it is necessary to locate a bore exactly parallel to, and at a set distance from, that previously machined in a link or connecting rod, one of the jaws may be removed and replaced by a locating mandrel, anchored in the T-slot of the chuck. The other three jaws are used to set up and hold the other end centrally. This principle may be extended to parts which may more conveniently be mounted on the lathe faceplate.

FIG. 8–5: Packing strips interposed between chuck jaws and work

FIG. 8–6: Chuck with one jaw reversed for centring big end of connecting rod

FIG. 8-7: Facing a rectangular piece with two of the chuck jaws reversed

Faceplate Mounting

Another operation which may call for reversing one or two jaws is machining rectangular parts as in Fig. 8-7. Not only work which is too large to be held in the chuck, but also that in which exact parallel location from flat back surface is required, may call for mounting on the faceplate. It is not always possible to ensure true parallelism of front and back surfaces when work is held in a chuck despite care in bedding the work against the jaw faces, because the tightening of the jaws may tend to tilt them slightly and force the work out of truth. A simple example of faceplate mounting is shown in the machining of a locomotive wheel in Fig. 8-8. The wheel casting is clamped by its flanged side agianst the faceplate, after ensuring that its back surface

is reasonably flat and free from rough high spots. It is held in position by two or more bolts and clamp plates between the spokes, and if the centre hole has already been drilled, it may be located by a plug mandrel fitted to the lathe mandrel socket. Otherwise, it will need to be set up by tapping it into position with a soft-faced hammer before the bolts are fully tightened.

FIG. 8-9: Gas engine fly-wheel mounted on the face-plate with wood backing

Generally, it is best to carry out all essential machining, including the turning of the tread and rim, facing the front, and boring the axle seating, all at this setting. The back face and the edge of the flange can then be machined afterwards by mounting the wheel on a mandrel.

A somewhat similar operation is shown in Fig. 8–9, namely the machining of a gas engine flywheel which is actually too large in diameter to be bedded directly against the faceplate. A wooden backplate has therefore been attached to the faceplate, by sunk bolts, and faced on the front surface after fixing. As before, bolts and clamp plates are used to hold the casting in position, and discretion was called for in tightening the bolts, as the spokes might easily be overstrained or cracked by excessive stress. The outer rim and face of the wheel, the integral flat pulley, and the centre bore, could then all be machined at one setting.

A somewhat more complicated casting, but still not very difficult to deal with, was the trunk column of the Stuart No. 10 steam engine, in which the top flange must be parallel, and the guide bore axis must be square, in relation to the mounting feet (Fig. 8–10). It was first checked to make certain that the casting would stand truly on the faceplate, with its axis vertical, and that the undersides of the feet were reasonably flat. (In some cases, preliminary filing or machining of

FIG. 8–10: Model steam engine trunk column casting set up on faceplate

the feet may be called for.) The casting was then clamped to the faceplate as shown, and set up to

FIG. 8–8: Turning the face and tread of a locomotive wheel on the faceplate

FIG. 8–11: Cylinder head attached to parallel packing piece, and set up on faceplate for centre-drilling and drilling valve ports

FIG. 8–12: Reaming a pair of crank discs, attached together and set up on the faceplate

FIG. 8–13: Integral crankpin and web attached to flat plate and set up on the faceplate

FIG. 8–14: Machining the port face of a steam engine cylinder on angle plate mounting

centralise the guide bore and the top flange for boring and facing them. After completing these operations, the casting was mounted on a mandrel in the reverse position for accurate facing of the foot surfaces.

Sometimes it is difficult either to hold components in a chuck or mount them directly on the faceplate. As an example, the cylinder head casting shown in Fig. 8–11 had a projection on its back surface which introduced difficulty in this respect. An aluminium disc, with a suitable recess to take the projection, was made and the casting was attached to it by four screws in holes which subsequently served to take the holding-down bolts. This mounting served a double purpose, as it was not only possible to set the casting centrally for machining the inside surface, but also (after marking out the locations) to offset it by sliding on the faceplate, to centralise the bores for inlet and exhaust valve ports and machine them truly, together with the valve seatings.

The ability to shift components without upsetting parallel location is one of the advantages of faceplate mounting when dealing with eccentric or offset machining operations. For instance, in fabricated crankshafts having webs in the form of discs or flat plates, true assembly may be assured by machining both of them together, while attached temporarily to each other by any convenient means, such as soft soldering. They are set up on the faceplate, first in the central position for boring the main journal seatings, and then offset to the crank throw radius for boring the crankpin seatings. This will ensure that when assembled, the complete shaft will run truly and in exact parallel alignment. A pair of crank discs (which will afterwards be cut away to form balance weights) is shown set up in this way in Fig. 8–12. Only one clamp is holding the work, for photographic reasons, as the second clamp obscured the view of the crankpin bore which is in process of being reamed to size.

Crankpins with integral flat-backed webs may be mounted directly on the faceplate, or on a parallel plate which can be shifted to adjust the radius. The example shown in Fig. 8–13 was located and prevented from turning on its axis by stop buttons fixed to the mounting plate and abutting against the balance weights on both sides while the turning and drilling of the crankpin journal was carried out.

Use of Angle Plates

For many operations, it is necessary to mount workpieces at right angles to a major reference surface. In most cases, the best way to do this is by attaching the work to a right-angled fixture or angle plate, mounted on the faceplate. A typical example of this method of setting up is shown in Fig. 8–14, where a steam engine cylinder casting, after boring, and facing the end flanges, needs to have the port face machined parallel to the major axis. The casting is attached to the angle plate by a single bolt through its bore, bearing on a flat plate which covers the full area of the end flange. In this particular case, only a facing operation on a flat surface was involved, so that it was not necessary to set the work exactly central. But in other cases it may be necessary to carry out a turning or boring operation on a part set up in this way, as in machining the port flange and boring the valve passage of the four-stroke cylinder head in Fig. 8–15 in which it was necessary to use a resilient packing piece between the component and the holding-down strap, to avoid crushing the delicate fins. The awkward shaped inlet pipe shown in

FIG. 8–15: Facing and boring valve passages on a petrol engine cylinder head

FIG. 8–16: Facing the flange of a curved pipe, mounted on angle plate

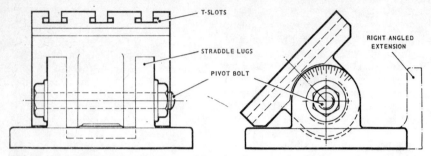

FIG. 8–17: Adjustable angle plate, with optional extension flange for acute-angle setting

Fig. 8–16 could hardly have been mounted in any other way than on an angle plate, and it was found necessary to make forked clamping plates to obtain a secure hold on the small area of the opposite end flange.

Sometimes it is necessary to mount work at an intermediate angle to its reference surface. Several forms of swivelling angle plates are available to deal with work of this nature, but it may be more convenient to make solid blocks of any convenient metal, or even hardwood, with angular faces, for mounting on the faceplate, and attaching the work at the correct angle. It is often possible to improvise, by superimposing one angle plate on another for machining small parts at odd angles. The

FIG. 8–18: Use of superimposed angle plates for holding work at various angles

boring and facing of a rotary admission valve port, illustrated in Fig. 8–18, was carried out with the aid of a fixture originally designed for internal machining of valve ports in part-spherical cylinder heads. For this purpose, the two parts of the fixture were connected by a pivot bolt located at the intersecting centre of the valve axes.

Other Faceplate Fixtures

The principle of the V-block is employed in several kinds of fixture for holding work parallel but eccentric to the lathe axis. One of the best known of these is the Keats V-angle plate (Fig. 8–19) which is made by Exe Engineering Co. Ltd., in various

FIG. 8–19: The Keats patent V-angle plate

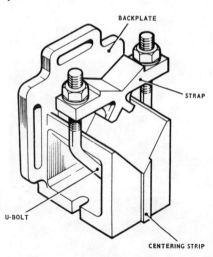

sizes for mounting on faceplates from 6 in. diameter upwards. It is seen in use, for eccentric boring of a component such as the eccentric sheave of a steam engine, in Fig. 8–20. A similar fixture (not commercially available) is shown in Fig. 8–21 machining the outside of an overhung crankpin. In both cases, the V-groove is machined parallel to the flat base, and at right angles to the back surface, so that it can be mounted to hold the work in either position. A reversible strap, or "strong-back", grooved on both sides to hold work over a wide range of diameters, is secured by a bent stirrup screwed and nutted at both ends.

There are many other fixtures employed for mounting components of awkward shape, or in various locations, on the faceplate, but these are generally in the nature of machining jigs, and specially constructed, so that their use is only justified when a number of pieces need to be positively located. Whatever kind of fixtures are employed, it is most important that their reference surfaces are true and that they are accurately located on the faceplate. It is easy to check the flatness and true running of the faceplate, and to correct it if necessary, but often the squareness of angle plates or other fixtures is taken

FIG. 8–20: Keats V-angle plate in use for boring an eccentric sheave

FIG. 8–21: Turning an overhung crank on Myford special V-angle plate

for granted, and in such cases they may perpetrate errors, instead of being aids to accuracy as they should be.

CHAPTER 9

BORING AND INTERNAL TURNING

THE term "boring" is used in engineering to denote the opening out or internal machining of a hole, rather than making a hole in solid material; the latter process is generally referred to as "drilling", and there is a distinction between the tools employed in the two cases. A further class of operation, known as "reaming", is often carried out for finishing or exact sizing of either drilled or bored holes. Castings and other preformed components often have holes initially produced by coring, blanking or piercing, which need to be bored to produce the necessary accuracy and finish for mechanical purposes. Single-point tools, comparable to those used for external turning, are normally employed for this work, and to distinguish it from other hole-forming methods, it may be defined as "internal turning", when dealing with concentric holes in work set up in the lathe chuck or on the faceplate. The basic shapes of these tools are shown in Fig. 9–1.

When holes have to be drilled concentrically in solid metal, it is necessary to provide a central location point on the work to ensure that the drill starts truly and follows the axial line without deviation. Various means have been used for this purpose, including the hand tool known as a "graver", shown in Fig. 9–2, which has a square shank ground to a fairly acute diamond point, so that the angular facet presents a cutting edge at approximately 60 degrees inclusive. This is steadied on a hand rest, as close as possible to the rotating work (which has previously been faced truly), and presented to it so as to cut an indentation in the exact centre. Some skill is necessary in the use of the graver to ensure that it cuts right into the true centre instead of leaving a "pip" as shown in Fig. 9–3, which would tend to displace the drill point rather than locating it truly. Many instrument makers and horologists still use the graver for this and other lathe operations, preferring it

FIG. 9–1: Basic shapes of internal turning tools

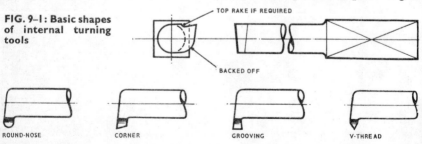

TOP RAKE IF REQUIRED

BACKED OFF

ROUND-NOSE   CORNER   GROOVING   V-THREAD

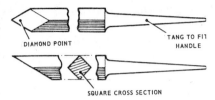

FIG. 9–2: A graver for centring holes or other hand turning operations

to any other methods of starting holes. But in general lathe practice, it has been superseded by quicker and more positive methods, generally employing tools fitted to the tailstock,

An acute-angled spearpoint drill, rigidly mounted in a short taper-shanked adaptor, is satisfactory for this purpose, but the most efficient tool is the "centre-drill", already referred to in Chapter 6, as a means of drilling the ends of work pieces for mounting between centres. This may be held in a drill chuck, provided that the alignment of the tailstock is beyond suspicion, but if it does not make contact with the exact centre of the work, it will tend to wobble, which may be difficult to correct. It is better to mount the centre drill in a rigid holder, as shown in Fig. 9–4, but this will be of no avail if there is any substantial misalignment of the tailstock. Should the point of the drill, when it first makes contact with the work, tend to trace a small circle, it is obviously out of line, and the tailstock will need adjustment to correct this. A slight error will not necessarily cause the centre-drill to run out of truth, but it will overload the fragile point, and cause risk of breakage.

The special advantage of the centre-drill, as a means of starting twist drills concentrically, is that it not only produces an accurate

FIG. 9–4: Centre-drill held in stub holder for starting a hole

countersink, but also a "pilot" which relieves the end load on the drill point and reduces any tendency to deviation. Wherever possible, the centre-drill should be fed in deep enough to locate the full diameter of the drill which follows it. In all drilling operations, but particularly centre-drilling, lubrication, and frequent backing-out to clear chips, are essential. It is often advisable, when large holes have to be drilled, to start with a small "pilot" hole and open it out by easy stages, rather than drilling to full size at one operation. This applies particularly to the use of light and relatively low-powered lathes, and especially those with mandrel bearings not equipped to cope with heavy end thrust.

Sometimes in spite of all precautions to start a drill truly, it is found

FIG. 9–3: The use of the graver for centring holes

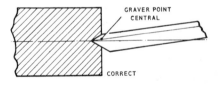

GRAVER POINT CENTRAL

CORRECT

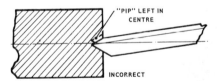

"PIP" LEFT IN CENTRE

INCORRECT

to wobble when it starts to cut. This may be corrected by means of a steady bar mounted in the tool post and brought into light contact with the drill. A bar with a V-groove in the end, at exact centre height, will have a more positive steadying effect than one with a plain square end. If possible, it should be brought into action before the lips of the drill have entered to their full depth. It will cause the drill to cut slightly large, and this is yet another reason for drilling undersize to start with. When the metal is not perfectly homogenous, or when cavities or cross holes are encountered, there is always risk of deviation in concentric drilling, and the truth of the drill should be carefully watched. In some cases, after undersize drilling, it may be found necessary to correct the size of the hole with a small boring tool before proceeding with a larger drill.

The fact that deviation of the drill is shown by visible wobble can be exploited to advantage, not only in normal concentric drilling, but also in ensuring true location and direction of other important drilling operations. When holes are drilled in a hand-guided appliance, or even in a drilling machine assumed to be reasonably accurate, it does not necessarily follow that the hole will start exactly in the required position, or that it will follow the intended axial line without deviation. For work in which accuracy of holes is highly important, therefore, it is a sound policy to set the component up in the lathe, using such aids to locate the centre of the hole as may be available, and to centre-drill, drill and (if necessary) bore it in position. This applies to operations such as drilling bearing bores, valve ports, and cylinder seatings.

Although twist drills are made accurately in graded sizes, neither the exact diameter nor the finish of the holes they produce is sufficiently accurate for important purposes. The use of a reamer, or a sizing tool of fixed or variable diameter, may be necessary to finish the hole. In most cases, reamers should only be used to take out a very small amount of metal, otherwise they are liable to snatch or chatter, producing holes which are neither smooth nor circular. The special reamers produced for machine operations are designed to cut mainly on the nose end, and will tolerate deeper cutting than hand reamers, for which the allowance should not be greater than about 0·005 in. on diameter for finishing. Keen and smooth cutting edges on reamers are essential for good finish, especially for metals such as tough bronze, in which the reamer is liable to seize if it is not cutting efficiently.

One of the simplest sizing tools is the D-bit, which is easily made in any size required, and will not only produce a true parallel hole, but also one which is axially straight. A form of D-bit has been adapted to drill deep holes from the solid, and another for finishing long bores for gun barrels, but the most useful type for general lathe work is one that serves as a substitute for a reamer. It can be made by turning or grinding a rod of tool steel to the required size (if not already available in the form of ground stock), and milling or filing it away to half its diameter

FIG. 9–5: D-bit with relief for chip clearance

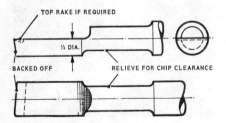

TOP RAKE IF REQUIRED

½ DIA.

BACKED OFF   RELIEVE FOR CHIP CLEARANCE

at the cutting end. It is then backed off on the front, with a slight radius at the corner, and finally hardened and tempered. Rake may be provided on the flat face if required, and it is often an advantage to provide relief, for the purpose of chip clearance, as shown in Fig. 9–5. No honing or other attempt to sharpen the side edges should be made, and regrinding when necessary should be done on the front cutting edge only. D-bits are extensively used in tool rooms, but are not as well known, or exploited as they deserve to be.

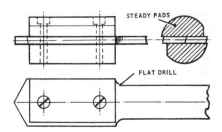

FIG. 9–6: A sizing drill for tailstock or tool post mounting

Another useful sizing tool is the floating reamer, which is made commercially in a range of sizes, for fitting to a tailstock holder which allows latitude of movement so that it can find its own alignment. It may be of fixed or adjustable diameter but in either case it is best suited for repetition work rather than occasional one-off jobs. Floating cutters (not truly classed as reamers) are sometimes made from flat tool steel, with cutting edges on both sides, and fitted loosely to a cross slot in a bar mounted in the tailstock. A flat drill may be used as a sizing tool, and to obtain a good finish, the fitting of steady pads of resilient fibre or hardwood, as shown in Fig. 9–6, is helpful.

With any form of sizing tool, the cutting edges must be keen and kept free from swarf. Lubrication is essential, except when working on cast iron. If one edge should become blunted, or metal build up on it, the tool may cut oversize or produce a rough finish. Whenever any considerable amount of metal needs to be removed in internal machining, it is most expeditious to use drills or other heavy duty tools for the major part of the operation. The type of tool known as a "core drill", and adapted to be mounted either in the tailstock socket or in the tool post,

is generally made in the form of a spearpoint drill with a specially rigid shank. It is particularly suited to boring out cored castings where lack of truth in the bore may tend to cause deviation of ordinary drills. Single-point boring tools, in view of their limited shank diameter, are always lacking in rigidity to some extent, and cannot take such heavy cuts as external tools.

In boring sleeves or bushes with relatively thin walls, there is a risk of distorting or crushing them by the pressure of the chuck jaws, and even when this effect is not perceptible, it may be found that the work is out of round when removed from the chuck. Sometimes this can be prevented by allowing extra length and plugging the work internally at the end held in the chuck, or by providing a thickened end of outer flange for chucking. The wastage of metal involved in this way can be justified as preferable to the risk of producing inaccurate work. Castings for making piston rings or cylinder liners are often made in the form of a "quill" or cored tube with a heavy flange, which helps to ensure soundness of metal in the moulding process, and also provides an adequate chucking piece for machining.

Components of this nature may with advantage be machined externally and internally at one setting, to ensure concentricity and uniform

FIG. 9–7: Casting with chucking flange machined externally and internally at one setting

wall thickness; the alternative method of locating from bore for turning the outside surface is appropriate only for light machining, especially if the bore has been highly finished. There is often some slight expansion caused by pressing a thin sleeve on a mandrel, which may lead to error in external sizing.

For "clearway" through boring, or running into an enlarged clearance chamber, a round-nosed tool is generally, but not invariably, best for obtaining a smooth and accurate bore. It will nearly always be found that some spring of the tool occurs in deep boring, and when nearing finished bore size, several passes of the tool at the same feed setting will continue to remove metal in gradually decreasing amount. With most lathes, necessary clearance of the saddle slide causes the tool to cut slightly deeper when traversing out

of the bore (i.e., to the right) than into it. If this is to be avoided, the feed of the cross slide must be relieved when retracting the tool from the hole.

When recess turning a rebate or recess with an internal corner, a side cutting tool must be used, but unless a really sharp internal corner is required, a slight radius on the tool point helps to ensure a smooth finish. For such operations as boring housings to fit ball or roller races, a slight fillet in the corner is usually permissible, but if not, a slight undercut in the extreme corner is advisable. When boring right through a disc or other component mounted directly on the faceplate, it is a prudent policy to back it up with sheet metal or even cardboard to reduce risk of running the tool into the faceplate. Backing is used, though not visible in Fig. 9–9, which shows an eccentric disc being bored on a Boxford lathe.

Saddle Boring

Some kinds of boring operations are best carried out by mounting the work on the cross slide of the lathe and using a rotating cutter. This applies to components which are large and cumbersome, or difficult to mount in a chuck or on the faceplate for any reason. For this work, a lathe having a flat boring table, with T-slots to facilitate holding down the workpiece, is preferable. It is necessary to locate the work with the bore horizontal, and exactly at the height of the lathe axis, by the use of parallel packing or other

FIG. 9–8: Recessing a bearing endplate with a side boring tool

convenient means. Setting up may be carried out by measurement from the base line, or checking from the existing bore, and the slide movement may be used to give sideways location.

A particular virtue of this method of boring is that by using a simple boring bar, or in some cases an overhung cutter in the chuck, the bore produced is bound to be exactly parallel—an important requirement for engine cylinders or pump barrels. But should there be any slack in the slides, side movement during the machining operation may cause circular error. The cross slide should be clamped, or its gib tightened, after the work has been located, and the saddle slide should be adjusted to the minimum clearance for traversing movement.

The depth of cut, and final sizing of the bore, are adjusted by setting the radius of the cutter. A simple method of fine adjustment is by mounting the driving end of the bar in a four-jaw chuck, so that by setting it very slightly eccentric for the final cut, the effective radius of the cutter is altered. With a boring bar located on the tailstock centre, this results in springing it slightly, and the method should not be used for coarse adjustment or heavy cutting operations.

As cutter bars, especially if they are of great length, are liable to some deflection, it is always advisable to use a bar of as large a diameter as possible. Its length is determined by that called for in traversing the work in relation to the cutter, and avoiding fouling either the tailstock at one end, or the driving gear at the headstock end.

A typical saddle boring operation operation is that shown in Fig. 9–11, namely, the boring of the endplate seatings in the crankcase of a small engine. These must obviously be exactly in line to locate the crankshaft bearing housings, and this is ensured by boring them both at one setting. Their faces must also be

FIG. 9–9: Boring an eccentric disc on 4¼-in. Boxford lathe

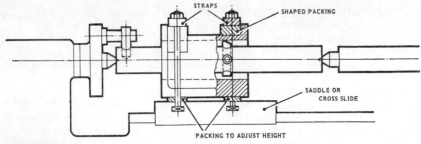

STRAPS
SHAPED PACKING
SADDLE OR CROSS SLIDE
PACKING TO ADJUST HEIGHT

FIG. 9–10: Casting set up on saddle or cross slide for boring with rotating tool

FIG. 9–11: Boring endplate seatings and crankcase register on engine body casting, mounted on lathe cross slide

FIG. 9–12: Limited clearance of solid and inserted-cutter tools

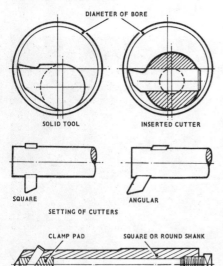

DIAMETER OF BORE

SOLID TOOL   INSERTED CUTTER

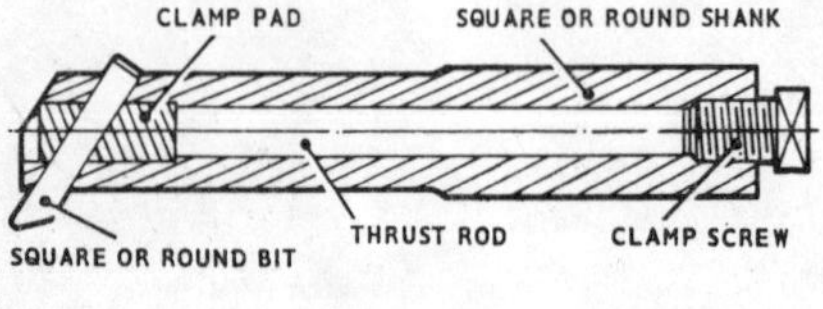

SQUARE   ANGULAR
SETTING OF CUTTERS

CLAMP PAD   SQUARE OR ROUND SHANK
SQUARE OR ROUND BIT   THRUST ROD   CLAMP SCREW

square with the bore, and this is most readily ensured by subsequent mounting of the component on a mandrel for the facing operations. It is possible to employ a boring head with radial movement for certain kinds of facing operations on the saddle, but in this particular instance such a fitting could only be used on the headstock end of the component.

Saddle mounting can also be usefully employed for machining convex or concave surfaces, such as those of a locomotive smokebox or a traction engine cylinder seating, using a cutter bar with a cutter which can be set to the required radius. End facing of work mounted on the cross slide can be carried out by means of a single-point fly cutter held in the lathe chuck, in conjunction with cross movement of the slide.

Internal Turning Tools

The single-point tools employed for boring are of various shapes to suit the nature of the work, and may be made either solid, with tips attached by brazing or welding, or in the form of boring bars with clamped cutter bits. For rapid re-

FIG. 9–13: Square and angular setting of cutters in boring bar

FIG. 9–14: A convenient form of holder for square or round cutter bits

moval of metal, a tool cutting mainly on the front edge is generally preferred, but a tool with a sharp corner should only be used if it is necessary to machine an internal shoulder where a fillet or radius is not permissible. The round-nosed tool is suitable for smooth finishing, and the square-nosed tool for recessing or internal grooving. Special shapes of tools may be necessary for dealing with certain kinds of work, and are generally ground to shape as and when required.

Tools made from solid, or with permanently attached tips, often have the cutting edge level with the top of the shank, and if mounted at correct cutting height, take up more room than is desirable in holes of limited size. In this respect, bars with inserted cutters are generally better, provided that the bits are short enough to avoid excessive projection. Various methods of clamping the cutter in the bar are employed as in Fig. 9–13; it is generally advisable to avoid projections from the bar at the cutting end, and set screws, if used here, should be sunk flush with the bar surface if possible. A hollow shank, with a set screw at the remote end, and a thrust rod, or alternatively, a draw bar and nut, for clamping the cutter, gives good security, but is less rigid than a solid shank. Either round or square cutter bits may be used, and they may either be fitted square with the shank, for dealing with straight-through boring operations, or set obliquely so that they can cope with a blind bore or internal shoulder.

Boring Tool Holders

Square or rectangular shanks of boring tools can, of course, be held directly in the tool post and adjusted for height by the means normally available, but round shank tools may call for the use of special holders.

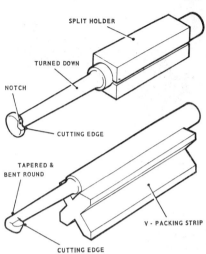

FIG. 9–15: Split holder for round shank boring tool

FIG. 9–16: V packing strip for round shank boring tools

The square section split holder shown in Fig. 9–15 is deservedly popular, but will only accommodate one size of round tool or cutter bar. A more adaptable method of holding round tools is shown in Fig. 9–16, consisting of a square block of steel with V-grooves in four sides. Not only will this hold tools of various sizes, at least as securely as the split holder, but by making the four grooves of different depths, it provides some measure of height adjustment.

Incidentally, the boring tool seen in Fig. 9–15 can be made by turning or grinding down a length of tool steel bar, and leaving a disc at the end which is notched on the grinding wheel to form the cutting edge. When reground, on the top cutting face only, this preserves the contour of the edge, and has a long life. The other tool, in Fig. 9–16, also made from round bar, involves a simple forging operation to bend round the end prior to shaping the edge.

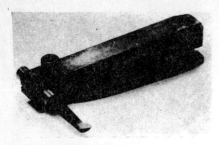

FIG. 9–17: Small boring tool held in split clamp of square shank holder

Round tools permit of rotation for slight adjustment of the cutting angles or height of the edge and are particularly useful for dealing with holes of small diameter.

Tool posts which provide for height adjustment by tilting movement of any kind may not be convenient for boring tools when operating in small bores. To maintain the axis of the tool horizontal when its height is adjusted, it may be mounted crosswise in a square holder with a split clamp as shown in Fig. 9–17. This particular holder (not commercially available) is adapted to suit the Myford rocker or "boat" but it is also suitable for other methods of tool post mounting. The tools are made from $\frac{1}{4}$ in. diameter tool steel bar, and provide ready access and visibility for boring small holes when mounted in this way. Tool holders which involve a good deal of overhang from the point of support (there are several patented forms of them) may provide convenient adjustment, but their rigidity for boring operations is open to suspicion. Nearly all boring tools, however rigidly mounted, are liable, by their very nature, to deflection under cutting load, and besides being made as stout as permissible for the size of the bore, should not project from the tool post farther than is necessary for the depth of the hole to be bored.

CHAPTER 10

SCREWCUTTING AND DIE THREADING

THE ability to cut threads of practically any pitch, either externally or internally, on the principles originated by Maudslay, is one of the most valuable properties of the metal turning lathe. A large proportion of components used in engine and machine construction entail the need for threads, either concentric to their axis or in related location to a reference surface. Of the various methods of producing threads, the screwcutting lathe offers the most positive method of ensuring true form and pitch, besides concentric accuracy, in all forms of screws, helices and spirals.

Orthodox screwcutting lathes involve the use of a sliding saddle, operated by means of a lead screw to move in a longitudinal direction, at a rate controlled by gearing, the ratio of which can be varied in relation to that of the work spindle or mandrel. If the gear ratio is 1: 1, so that the mandrel and lead screw rotate at the same speed, a tool point presented to the work will trace a helix of the same pitch as the lead screw. By varying the gear ratio, other pitches can be obtained in proportion. The simplest method of obtaining the required ratio is by using different combinations of gearing, set up on adjustably mounted spindles, to transmit the drive from the mandrel to the lead screw. Though change-speed gearboxes are

commonly used on modern lathes to simplify the selection of various gear ratios, the same principles of operation still apply.

It is usual to provide some means of disengaging the lead screw drive to the saddle, either by fitting a split clasp nut to the saddle apron, or alternatively, some form of positive engagement clutch in the lead screw drive. Some of the small, simple types of screwcutting lathes employ a dog or pin clutch, in conjunction with a solid lead screw nut attached to the saddle. In either case it is important that engagement of the drive should only be possible in *one* rotational position of the lead screw. Some lathes have been made with no provision for disengaging the drive, so that they need to be run backwards and forwards throughout the entire screwcutting operation, but this is not convenient for general lathe work.

Screwcutting Gear Trains

The set of change wheels supplied with a screwcutting lathe is arranged to cover as wide a range of gear ratios as possible, including all or most of those required for cutting the standard threads encountered in general practice. It is of course essential that all the gears in a complete gear train should be of the same tooth pitch (that is, the same circumferential distance between any

FIG. 10-1: Screwcutting gear train on Myford

two teeth), but the pitch employed, and the number of teeth in individual gears in a set, also their diameter, vary in different lathes. A comparatively small number of gears, suitably arranged, will provide permutations covering a very wide number of screw pitches. The gears are set up on spindles which can be mounted on a slotted bracket, sometimes termed a gear quadrant, or "banjo", so that their distance apart can be adjusted to enable gears of different sizes to be assembled in correct mesh. Fig. 10-1.

Many small and medium size lathes have lead screws of eight threads per inch, and a suitable set of change wheels may have the following numbers of teeth: 20, 25, 30, 35, 38, 40, 45, 50, 55, 60, and 65. One or more of these gears, usually those with 20 or 40 teeth, may be duplicated for convenience in setting up, making a set of twelve gears in all. This covers most requirements, but additional gears can be supplied which will extend the range still further.

The gear ratios obtained by various arrangements of the change wheels may be determined by the proportional numbers of teeth in the *driving* and *driven* gears respectively.

For the simplest arrangement, it may be assumed that the gear wheel on the mandrel meshes directly with that on the lead screw. If the former has 20 teeth and the latter has 40 teeth, this gives a reduction of 2: 1, so that in conjunction with an 8 t.p.i. lead screw, the pitch of the thread produced is 16 t.p.i. The same result is produced by a combination of 25–50, or 30–60. A gear of 40 teeth meshing with one of 50 teeth will give a reduction of 5: 4, to produce 10 t.p.i. If the positions of the gears are reversed, the same ratios will produce an *increase* instead of a reduction, though this is much less commonly required for normal screwcutting purposes.

As it is not normally possible to mesh the gears on the mandrel directly together, because of the distance between them, it is necessary to interpose other gears between them, of suitable size to enable them to be meshed with both gears by adjusting the position of the spindles and the angle of the mounting bracket. The number of teeth in any intermediate gears which mesh simultaneously with driving and driven gears in the train, are immaterial, as they do not affect the ultimate gear ratio. Such gears are therefore known as "idlers" and a train set up in this way is known as a "simple" train of gears.

The diagram (10–2) shows the essential features of a simple train in which it is assumed that the work is rigidly coupled to the mandrel, which also carries the driving gear A; the lead screw has a solid nut which propels the sliding saddle, and with it, the cutting tool, also a driven gear C mounted directly on its outer end. An idler wheel B of any con-

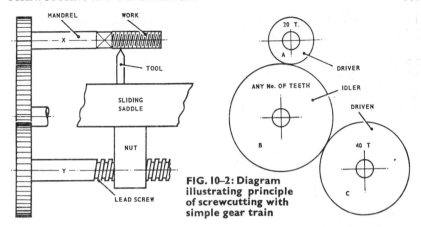

FIG. 10–2: Diagram illustrating principle of screwcutting with simple gear train

venient size runs loosely on its spindle and meshes with both A and B. For a given pitch of the lead screw Y, the thread generated at X will be equal to the ratio of A : C.

In many instances it is not possible to obtain the required pitch for a particular thread by means of a simple train, and it is necessary to use two or more stages of gearing, as shown in Fig. 10–3, where the intermediate spindle carries two gears of different sizes, keyed or otherwise attached to each other, though still running loosely on the spindle. The driver A, in the example shown, having 20 teeth and meshing with

the 40-t. driven [gear B, gives a reduction of 2: 1, while the 30-t. second driving gear C, running at the same speed as B, meshing with the the second driven gear D, of 45 teeth, gives a further reduction of 3: 2. The total gear ratio, therefore, is (2: 1 × 3: 2), or 3: 1, which in conjunction with an 8 t.p.i. lead screw, will produce a thread of 24 t.p.i. This particular thread could have been obtained with a simple train of, say, 20 and 60, but it illustrates the principle of "compound" gear trains.

It is frequently necessary to double or even triple the gear stages in a

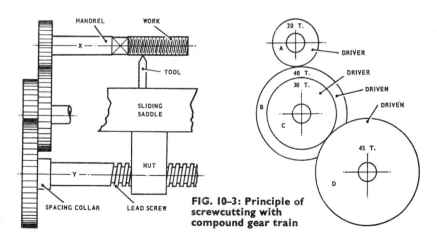

FIG. 10–3: Principle of screwcutting with compound gear train

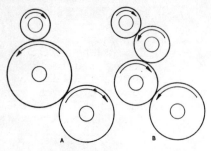

FIG. 10–4: Diagram showing reversal of lead screw rotation by varying the number of stages in gear train

compound train, but the principles still apply, and the ratio of the gearing is still determined by the numbers of teeth in the driving gears, in relation to those in the driven gears. Expressed in arithmetical terms, the drivers form the numerators, and the driven gears the denominators; for example:

$$\frac{\text{Drivers } 30 \times 20}{\text{Driven } 45 \times 60} = \frac{2}{9}.$$

With a lead screw of $\frac{1}{8}$ in. pitch, the thread produced is $\frac{2}{9 \times 8} = \frac{1}{36}$ in. or in other words, 36 t.p.i. Makers of lathes usually supply screwcutting charts for use with the gears in their standard set, but if this is not available, a knowledge of simple arithmetic will enable the operator to work out most gear trains for himself; and indeed this knowledge is essential for many workshop calculations, apart from screwcutting.

When there is only a single stage, or an odd number of stages in the gear train, whether simple or compound, the lead screw will turn in the same direction as the mandrel (Fig. 10–4a). Most lathes are so arranged that clockwise rotation of the lead screw at the driving gear end traverses the saddle to the right when the clasp nut or clutch is engaged. Under these conditions, movement

of the cutting tool will produce a left-hand helix. To reverse the rotation of the lead screw, it is necessary to provide an even number of stages in the complete gear train (Fig. 10–4(b)). In some simple lathes, the only provision made for this is an extension of the change wheel bracket, or a lug on the headstock, for the accommodation of the extra gear spindle. But on more completely equipped lathes, a tumbler or cluster gear assembly is fitted as in Fig. 10–1, which enables the gear train to be instantly reversed or disengaged. This is usually of the spur gear type, fitted directly under, and engaging with, a fixed gear on the end of the mandrel. The output shaft of the tumbler gear usually runs at the same speed as the mandrel.

An alternative form of reversing gear consists of a bevel gear cluster axially coupled to the lead screw. This has the advantage that, as it normally runs slower than the mandrel, it can safely be engaged when the lathe is running, but on the other hand, it keeps the gear train in

FIG. 10–5: Principle of screwcutting dial indicator

INDICATOR DIAL

LEAD SCREW

WORM WHEEL

running engagement with the mandrel, which is not always desirable.

Apart from lathes of the larger and more elaborate types, which often have screwcutting gearboxes incorporated, most of the lathes within the scope of this book employ lead screws of 8 t.p.i., though some older and now obsolete types had 10 t.p.i. lead screws. Charts to suit these lead screws are given in the Appendices, but it is not thought necessary to include charts for other pitches, which are now rare. It should be noted that even when the pitch of the lead screw, and the numbers of teeth in the change wheels, are known, screwcutting charts cannot always be worked out without inspection of the particular lathe, because the design of the change wheel bracket, and its slots or other provision for fitting the gear spindles, influences their arrangement. With compound trains, offsetting of the gears is involved, and it is necessary to avoid fouling of gear teeth with those on adjacent shafts which are not intended to be engaged.

With the imminent likelihood of metric threads being more widely, or perhaps almost exclusively, employed in the near future, there is a possibility that metric thread lead screws may be fitted to British lathes. It should be observed, however, that existing fractional-pitch lead screws may be used to cut metric threads by the addition of extra change wheels, but it is a more complicated matter to cut fractional-pitch threads with a metric lead screw.

Picking up Threads

Screwcutting operations generally involve taking a number of cuts with gradually increased cross feed. It is of course essential that the tool should traverse the same path each time, or in other words, "pick up"

the partially cut thread accurately. If the thread being cut is a multiple of the lead screw pitch, this happens automatically so long as the top slide is not moved, and that there is no undue slack in the slides which may cause erratic movement. With an 8 t.p.i. lead screw, threads of 8, 16, 24, 32, 40 and 48 t.p.i. can be cut by engaging the lead screw at *any* position of saddle traverse or mandrel rotation. But for other pitches, the lead screw can only be engaged in a certain juxtaposition of mandrel, lead screw and saddle traverse if double-tracking or "split threading" is to be avoided.

One way of avoiding risk in this respect is to keep the lead screw engaged throughout the number of passes required to cut the thread to full depth. This involves the need to reverse the rotation of the lathe to run the tool back to its starting point after each pass, after the cross feed has been retracted to take the tool out of engagement. For small lathes driven either by treadle or a reversing motor, this is often the most convenient method for short threads, always provided that the chuck or driver plate can be prevented from unscrewing. But for long threads, or on heavy lathes, it may be slow and tedious, and more

FIG. 10–6: Wiring diagram for electrical screwcutting indicator

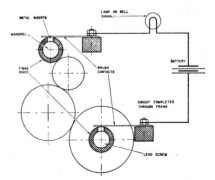

efficient means of ensuring correct re-engagement of the lead screw may be preferred.

The old method of making chalk marks on the mandrel and lead screw gear wheels, and engaging the clasp nut or clutch only when both marks were in the correct relative positions, is obviously open to some risk of error. It has been superseded in modern practice by the dial indicator, incorporated in or attached to the sliding saddle, and actuated by a worm gear engaged with the lead screw. This can only be used on lathes which have a clasp nut or other means of disengaging the lead screw from the saddle traverse. When the saddle is stationary and the lead screw is rotating, the dial will turn at a rate determined by the screw pitch and the number of teeth in the worm gear, but when the clasp nut is engaged to traverse the saddle, it ceases to turn. It thus serves as a positive means of indicating the position of the saddle in relation to the rotation of the lead screw. Fig. 10–5.

If the lead screw has eight threads per inch and the worm wheel has sixteen teeth, there will be two positions on the dial at which the lead screw can be engaged for any whole number of threads per inch to be cut. For any even number of t.p.i., there are four positions on the dial; and for multiples of 4 t.p.i., eight positions. Only one position of engagement is possible for threads involving odd halves, such as $7\frac{1}{2}$ or $15\frac{1}{2}$ t.p.i., and the dial does not cover any further subdivisions, approximate or metric pitches. These, however, are comparatively rare in normal lathe practice, and would call for much more complicated instrumentation.

Lathes having a solid nut in permanent engagement with the lead screw, with a dog clutch for coupling it with the driving gears, cannot be fitted with a dial indicator of the above type. So far as is known, no mechanical device for indicating the clutch engagement position has ever been applied to such lathes but it is possible to fit a simple form of electrical indicator which will show the correct relative positions of mandrel and lead screw. Contact-making devices are fitted to the respective shafts, which establish a closed circuit only in one position of rotation, and either an audible signal, by a bell or buzzer, or a visible one, by an indicator lamp, are thus operated. With a device of this nature, the saddle must always be run back to exactly the same position on the bed for engaging the drive. Fig. 10–6.

During any screwcutting operation, the gear train must be kept in positive engagement, including the tumbler or other reversing gear. Spur gears cannot be run in tight engagement, and when setting them up, a slight degree of clearance in the teeth must be allowed. This will introduce a certain amount of backlash, or lost motion in the drive, but no harm will be done so long as the cutting load is always in one direction under normal conditions of screwcutting, and the tool is always backed out clear of the thread for returning to starting point. Gear spindles should be kept lubricated, but oil or grease on gear teeth is messy and should be very sparingly applied if at all, except for continuous heavy duty, in which case gears are usually enclosed in an oil bath. Swarf or other foreign matter must be excluded from the gearing.

Self-acting Feeds

Simple screwcutting lathes usually employ the lead screw for self-acting feeds, and compound gear trains are generally used to provide a sufficiently

FIG. 10–7: Moore & Wright angle gauge for screwcutting tools

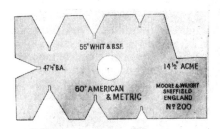

high reduction ratio for the feeds required. It is possible to obtain feeds as fine as 0·0025 in. per revolution of the mandrel by the use of triple compound gearing, but sometimes special methods of obtaining a high reduction ratio by the use of worm or differential gearing are employed. Means of changing over quickly from a screwcutting train to one giving a much finer self-acting feed, and thus saving time in combined operations, have been devised. The finer feeds are most useful when taking radially deep cuts with ripping tools or running-down cutters, but it is a mistake to assume that high finish is best obtained by using extremely fine feeds. Very often a broad, well-rounded tool, with moderate feed, will produce the most satisfactory results.

The more elaborate lathes often employ a separate shaft for operating the self-acting feed, or have a longitudinal keyway in the lead screw for driving a floating worm, for this purpose. In these lathes, the saddle drive is usually taken through the rack gearing instead of the clasp nut. While on the subject of self-acting feed, its application to the cross slide may be mentioned. This is very useful for dealing with broad surfacing cuts, but it calls for a good deal of complication in the gearing of the lathe apron, which is not usually justified in the simpler and less expensive lathes. When separate gearing is employed for screwcutting, traversing and cross feeding, it is important that interlocks should be fitted, to prevent any two motions to be simultaneously engaged, as this could cause considerable damage to all parts of the mechanism.

Tool Setting

The tools for internal or external screwcutting should be ground to the correct form, and presented to the work at correct height, and square to the work axis. The application of a thread angle gauge such as that shown in Fig. 10–7 is useful, not only for grinding the tool to correct form, but also for setting it truly in

PARALLEL MANDREL BETWEEN CENTRES

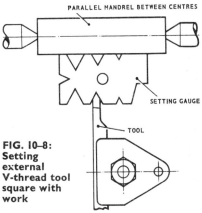

SETTING GAUGE

TOOL

FIG. 10·8: Setting external V-thread tool square with work

the tool post. When setting an external screwcutting tool, the gauge may be laid against the side of the work, or a parallel mandrel mounted in the chuck, or between centres, for this purpose. This may not be possible when setting internal tools, due to limitations of cross traverse, in which case the side of the gauge may be laid against a driver plate or faceplate, as shown in Fig. 10–9. Rake and clearance angles for screw-cutting tools should follow normal principles, but as they have to clear the helix angle of the thread, they should have greater clearance on the leading flank (according to whether right- or left-hand threads are to be cut). Generally it is sufficient to use a tool with rather more clearance than usual, unless the helix angle is coarse, when the tool should be specially ground for the particular pitch. This applies particularly to multi-start threads or worms. A tool with a round shank, fitted to a holder or V packing block so that it can be rotated to suit the helix angle, will cope with threads of any pitch, but it should be noted that the form of the tool, and that of the thread cut, is influenced when it is rotated to any substantial angle.

The mandrel speed employed in screwcutting is generally limited by control requirements, including the disengagement of the clasp nut or the withdrawal of the tool at the end of the cut. It is usual to run the lathe in back gear when screwcutting, if only for this reason. Lathes equipped with special means of automatic tool control can be run at the same speed as for normal cutting operations, but this does not apply to any of the machines described in this book.

Thread Forms

The most widely used V-threads in Britain follow the form introduced by Sir Joseph Whitworth, having an included flank angle of 55 degrees and a radius at both root and tip. Other V-threads include BA, with flanks at $47\frac{1}{2}$ degrees, and the International Metric thread, at 60 degrees. The same angle is employed in Sellers or U.S. standard threads, which are truncated, or in other words, flat at both root and tip. The tools for cutting these threads must be ground to the approximate angles, but it is generally permissible to reduce the radius, or extend the depth at the tip, for both external and internal threads, to simplify the tools and give clearance at root and tip. Truncated threads are increasingly employed in industrial production, especially when produced by taps and dies, as they reduce the amount of metal which needs to be removed, thereby making machining easier, without appreciably reducing the strength of the threads.

Square threads are used for many purposes, including presses, vices and clamping appliances, which are repeatedly used, and subjected to heavy end thrust. The tools used for cutting them are ground similar to parting tools, except that the front face must necessarily be square instead of angular. It is not generally desirable to make the cutting end deeper than is necessary for cutting the thread to full depth, with

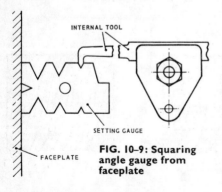

FIG. 10–9: Squaring angle gauge from faceplate

FIG. 10–10: Some of the common thread forms employed in engineering practice

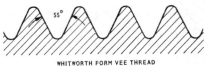

WHITWORTH FORM VEE THREAD

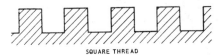

SQUARE THREAD

ACME THREAD

BUTTRESS THREAD

reasonable allowance for regrinding, in order to retain maximum rigidity; and for the same reason, solid ground tool bits are preferable to narrow blades, which are subject to side deflection. When working with readily machinable materials, the tool may with advantage be made exactly to the width of the required cut (i.e., half the pitch for single-start threads), but sometimes it is easier to gash the threads with a narrow tool, and finish with one of full width, or by side adjustment of the tool. In some cases it is permissible to allow clearance at top or bottom of a square thread, in which case, the depth of cut is not critical. But when minimum radial clearance is required, it is advisable to make either the screw or the nut longer than necessary, and turn or bore a "witness" to fit the root or crest diameter, as the case may be, to act as a guide for the depth of feed of the screwcutting tool. The unwanted length of material is afterwards cut away.

Small internal square threads often present difficulties in screwcutting, because of the small clearance allowable for backing out the tool, which can only have a small shank, and is

FIG. 10–11: Cutting a left-hand Acme thread on Myford ML7 lathe

FIG. 10–12: Single, double and three-start square threads

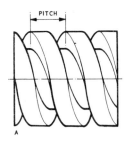

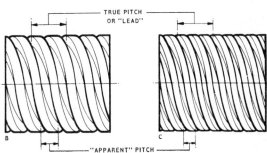

FIG. 10–13: Two stages in screwcutting a 2-start square thread taper tap blank

therefore very fragile. It is often worth while to make a tap, in the form of a replica of the external thread, in tool steel, with flutes and cutting edges, hardened and tempered. If made with a long taper, this will cut the thread efficiently, and will often produce better results than can be obtained by internal screwcutting. Fig. 10–13.

Acme form threads are also suitable for heavy duty, and with slight adaptation, can be employed for worm gearing. They are cut in much the same way as square threads, and gashing in with a narrow square thread tool is desirable before applying the 29-degree forming tool. Buttress threads are used for heavy duty where major end thrusts are always in one direction, such as in certain kinds of vice screws. The pressure face of the thread is square with the axis, or slightly undercut, while the angle of the flank depends on the depth of thread in relation to the pitch.

Multi-start Threads

The type of thread used for most constructional fittings consists of a single spiral groove extending throughout the length of the screwed part. For obtaining maximum strength and screw thrust, the "single-start" thread is generally best and easiest to produce, but for some purposes, increased pitch of the

thread is required, without excessive depth, and threads having two or more "starts" are used. These have a greater pitch angle than normal threads, and the *apparent* pitch, or distance, between adjacent threads, is less than the true pitch or "lead", according to the number of starts.

It is possible to cut multi-start threads by means of special chasers or ganged cutting tools, which cut the required number of starts at once. But if single-point cutting tools are used, it is necessary to index the work in the required number of positions for the required number of starts. This can be done, in work mounted between centres, by using indexing driving devices, such as a number of equally spaced driving pins in the driver plate. For chuck work, the same result may be achieved by mounting the chuck on an indexed backplate or adaptor.

Multi-start threads arc uscd on many quick-acting feed or adjusting screws, focusing movements of cameras etc., and may be adapted to the cutting of low ratio worm gears, and skew or spiral gearing. When the helix angle is considerable, it is usually more efficient to cut them by thread milling appliances than by the use of single or multi-point tools.

Hand and Machine Chasers

The term "chaser", in lathe practice, is generally understood to mean a multi-point form tool for cutting or finishing threads, as distinct from

the type of hand tool used by jewellers and silversmiths. Machine chasers such as that shown in Fig. 10–14 are held in the tool post, and used in much the same way as single-point screwcutting tools, but their principal application is in production work rather than general workshop practice. Hand chasers, in the past, have been extensively used for producing threads from the solid, on lathes not equipped for screwcutting, by moving them sideways by hand at the rate required to generate the required pitch. This kind of work calls for a great deal of manipulative skill, and even at best is somewhat haphazard; it has largely become obsolete with the availability of machines equipped with more positive and efficient means of cutting threads.

The use of hand chasers is now usually confined to the finishing, and possibly sizing of, external and internal threads. Single-point screwcutting tools cannot produce the complete form of V-threads which require a radius at the tip, though a slight rounding off, sufficient for practical purposes, may be obtained by the use of a fine file while the lathe is running. A chaser should, however, be used wherever available for this purpose. Either a hand rest, or a flat piece of metal held in the tool post at a suitable height, may be used to support the chaser, as shown in Fig. 10–15. It should be as close to the work as possible, to avoid any tendency of the tool to tilt or snatch, and both the surface of the rest, and the underside of the chaser, should be smooth so that it will slide freely. A long handle fitted to the chaser will assist in providing leverage and control of the cutting angle.

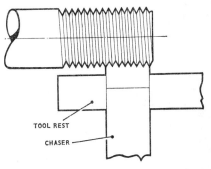

TOOL REST

CHASER

FIG. 10–15: Using external hand chaser

For internal chasing, the rest should be set at right angles to the work, as close to the end of it as possible. It is difficult to chase deep threaded holes in this way, as the chaser lacks positive support, and it is advisable to do as little internal chasing as possible. Machine chasers for internal work can be made similar to a screw tap, smaller than the hole, and with a long rigid shank which can be held in the lathe tool post.

FIG. 10–16: Using internal hand chaser

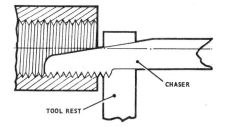

CHASER

TOOL REST

A method of chasing which has survived since the early days of metal turning lathes is that which employs a short thread, known as a "hob", mounted on the lathe mandrel, to traverse the chaser at the required pitch rate. A bar working in sliding bearings, parallel to the lathe mandrel, is usually employed to carry arms at either end for mounting the chaser, and also the segmental nut or "follower", which can thus be brought into engagement with the hob. An adjustable stop can be fitted to the chaser arm to limit its radial movement, and thus control the depth of thread. A different hob and follower must be used for each different pitch of thread. This method, though primitive, is accurate and expeditious, and is often used on capstan lathes employed for small and moderate quantity production.

Angular Feed

The loading on the tool point,

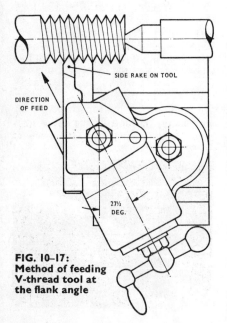

SIDE RAKE ON TOOL

DIRECTION OF FEED

27¼ DEG.

**FIG. 10–17:
Method of feeding
V-thread tool at
the flank angle**

when cutting V-threads, is very heavy, especially when the threads are coarse and deep. There is often risk of breaking the tool point under these conditions, even with moderate feed. To reduce this risk, and promote cutting efficiency, it is helpful to feed the tool in at the angle of one of its flanks. The top slide is swivelled to the flank angle, $27\frac{1}{2}$ degrees to the cross slide axis in the case of Whitworth form threads, as shown in Fig. 10–17. The cross slide should be used for withdrawing the tool at the end of the cut, but it should be returned to the same position each time, and cutting feed applied by the top slide only. It is possible to take advantage of top rake, applied more or less at right angles to the cutting flank of the tool, to ease load and obtain maximum cutting efficiency.

When starting V-threads, a tracer cut may be taken at a radial depth of about 0·010 in., but it will usually be found advisable to reduce this to half the amount on the next pass, and as the tool penetrates deeper, to reduce it gradually still further down to 0·001 in. or less on the final cuts. Square threads, however, may be cut with a constant feed depth of 0·005 in. except for the finishing cut. The rigidity of the lathe mandrel and slides, also their condition and adjustment, will affect the amount of feed which can safely be applied, and lathes in bad condition, or with worn lead screws and nuts, may make any screwcutting operations precarious, to say the least.

Finishing ends of threads

At the starting end of a thread, it is generally advisable to provide a chamfer or bevel to assist in engaging the mating thread. This can be done with the flank of the tool, either before or after the thread is cut. The

FIG. 10–18: Finishing the ends of internal and external threads

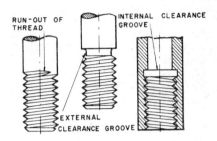

RUN-OUT OF THREAD

INTERNAL CLEARANCE GROOVE

EXTERNAL CLEARANCE GROOVE

finishing end of the thread should, where possible, run out into a clearance deep enough to clear the tip of the tool. But in shafts or other parts which are heavily stressed, deep undercuts may cause serious weakness, or provide a focus for subsequent cracks. This risk can be reduced by using a tool with a round nose to form the clearance groove, but for maximum strength, it is best to finish the thread by withdrawing the tool more or less gradually at the end of the cut. A certain degree of skill is required to do this neatly, and if the thread should over-run when nearing full depth, the tool may be strained or broken. Devices for withdrawing the tool automatically at the critical point have been produced, but are not at all common in normal lathe practice.

For checking the accuracy of both form and pitch of threads being cut, or identifying sample threads, the use of a standard screw pitch gauge as shown in Fig. 10–19 is recommended.

Use of Taps and Dies

Standard threads for bolts, nuts and similar purposes, which do not call for specially high precision, can most conveniently be cut in the lathe by taps and dies of good quality. If these are presented to turned or bored work in true axial alignment, they will generally cut a thread sufficiently accurately for all but the most exacting work. A taper on the end of the work, or an internal chamfer in a hole, will assist in getting the die or tap to start truly. Most ordinary dies are "throated", or tapered at the entry, so that they will not cut a parallel thread right up to a shoulder on the work. This may

often be corrected by reversing the die after cutting the initial thread, but in all cases where parts have to screw right home against a shoulder, a clearance groove or recess in either the external or internal component should be provided.

Taps may be held in a drill chuck to present them truly to the work, and where the nature of the work permits, a taper tap may be used to start the cut, as in ordinary procedure. Dies need to be fitted to a tailstock holder as shown in Fig. 10–21 and should preferably be provided with free sliding motion, so that they are neither dragged nor forced against their normal pitch rate by tailstock feed movement. Considerable torque is often involved in cutting threads with taps and dies, especially if they are large or coarse, and the usual key fitted to the tailstock barrel may be overloaded, or the friction grip of the

FIG. 10–19: Use of standard screw pitch gauge for checking form and pitch of threads

socket fitting become inadequate to cope with this. Some means of taking the torque directly on the die holder, such as a radial lever or other projection, may be used to relieve this load.

In the tailstock die holder shown in Fig. 10–22, the die head is a sliding fit on the parallel part of the shank, so that it is free to move endwise. The cutting torque is taken through two or more dogs or pins, to a radial torque lever. Standard size circular dies can be fitted, and the usual three screws for adjusting them are fitted to the head. The shank is hollow, so that small bar stock can be run right through it if required, but for short threads, uniformity of length can be obtained by setting the internal limit stop. When in operation, the die is started by advancing the tailstock

feed screw and following up the die for the required length of thread. Arresting the feed, whether by contact of the limit stop with the end of the work, or otherwise, will cause the die head to run off the pins, and thus disengage from the torque lever.

The particular advantages of this die holder are that it allows the die to progress at its natural pitch rate, without any constraint from either the tailstock feed or the torque lever. Spare die heads, with pre-set or different sized dies, can instantly be fitted, and any number of parts can be threaded to exactly the same length. It is possible to adapt the same general principles to tailstock tap holders, though other methods of arresting the feed movement, to ensure threads of exact depth, would need to be used.

Dies of the expanding type, which open at the end of the cut, so as to allow them to be withdrawn without reversal of motion, are recommended for efficiency and speed of operation, but they are relatively expensive tools, more appropriate to use on machines for quantity production

FIG. 10–22: A tailstock die holder with slip drive and stop to regulate length of thread

FIG. 10–21: Myford tailstock die holder for standard circular dies, in operation

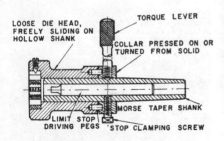

than general-purpose lathes.

The same applies to collapsing taps, which are normally made only in comparatively large sizes.

Where extreme concentric accuracy in either external or internal threads are called for, such as on running shafts or in collars or bushes, dies or taps should not be relied upon to produce sufficiently close limits of truth. Screwcutting, on work initially true, produces more positive accuracy, but even so, some form of *plain* parallel or tapered register is recommended when the highest possible precision is necessary.

CHAPTER 11

MISCELLANEOUS LATHE OPERATIONS

THE foregoing chapters describe most of the operations which are encountered in normal lathe work, but there are many others of a more or less unorthodox nature which need to be dealt with occasionally. Although in industrial practice, special-purpose machines are generally available to cope with these operations, there are many workshops in which the only machine tool ready to hand is the lathe. Both amateur and professional turners often find it helpful to exploit the versatility of the lathe and the ability to adapt it to practically any machine tool process.

A good deal of individual initiative and ingenuity has been devoted to the design of special attachments to the lathe, and the methods and appliances originally developed for use with horological and instrument lathes can often be applied to larger scale engineering work. It is not within the scope of this book to describe in detail the more elaborate attachments employed for milling, keyseating, gearcutting, etc., but they are fully described in the handbook *Milling in the Lathe*, and have also been the subject of many articles in the *Model Engineer* at various times. But even with the very simplest of machine tool fixtures, or with standard lathe equipment already available, it is possible to carry out many operations such as face milling and flycutting with facility and accuracy equal to that attainable on other machine tools.

There are many workers who object to what they call "gadgetry" in any shape or form, while others go to the opposite extreme and make attachments for every conceivable purpose. It is generally advisable to strike the happy medium in this matter, and consider the practical usefulness of any appliance it is proposed to construct, in relation to the time and cost it involves. Obviously it is uneconomical to spend much time and trouble on an appliance only adaptable to a single operation, which is not likely to recur very often, if at all. A simple device working on a sound basic principle is often the best solution to a difficult machining problem.

The same applies to all special-purpose jigs and cutting tools; it is often thought that jigs are only necessary in quantity production work, but this is not necessarily true. Any device which will facilitate positive accuracy, or present either the work or the tool in definite location for machining, is worth while considering, though of course its usefulness will be enhanced if it is applicable to the production of a number of similar products.

Spherical Turning

It is often necessary to turn work which involves spherical curves on some part of its surface. Complete spheres are difficult to produce by normal turning methods, though special chucking devices are employed in the production of such objects as billiards balls, often by hand turning tools. But normally this is not necessary, because metal balls can be obtained ready-made to high precision, in practically all sizes. In much of the spherical-curved work turned in the lathe, precision of form is not highly important. Such objects as knobs and ball handles for machine controls, switches and similar purposes, need only be approximately spherical, and it is sufficient for them to be well finished and to look right. They can often be turned by form tools, though if these involve any considerable breadth they may be difficult to use in light lathes without risk of chattering or digging in. The shape may be formed roughly by manipulation of the slide-rest tools, and finished by a hand tool, using a radius gauge or template as a guide to the finished shape.

When it is necessary to turn a fairly accurate spherical shape, such as in producing a ball-and-socket joint which must work smoothly and without slack in any position, the form can be generated by a tool having a movement around a fixed pivot. Several kinds of spherical turning appliances have been produced, some of which employ a vertical pivot, and others a horizontal pivot, in a fixture set at exact centre height at the front or back of the work. These are worth while if there is any considerable amount of spherical turning to be done, but for coping with an occasional job, the simple device shown in Fig. 11–1 will be found quite adequate. It consists of a flat bar which forms a hand lever, pivoted to a bolt anchored to the cross slide of the lathe, and carrying a small tool post which provides some measure of radial adjustment.

The pivot bolt is clamped in a fixed position on the slide, and fitted with a bush which should preferably provide a frictional fit for the lever, such as by the use of a spring washer. One or more holes at different radii in the lever, according to the size of spheres to be turned, are used to secure the tool fixture. In any device of this nature, it is necessary to locate the pivot truly in line with the centre of the work in both the axial and cross planes. To this end, the T-bolt is made

FIG. 11–1: The use of a simple pivoted lever appliance for external and internal spherical turning

hollow, and fitted with a removable gauge pin, with a point which can be lined up with the live centre of the lathe before the work is mounted for machining. It is permissible to move the slides for traversing and feeding movements, but they must be returned to the set positions for finishing the spherical curve. If this is not done, oblate or barrel-shaped spheroids will be produced, according to whether the pivot is displaced to the front or rear of the lathe axis.

The gauge pin can also be used for setting the radius of the tool point for the required spherical diameter, due allowance being made for the radius of the pin itself. Alternatively, it may be cut away for half its diameter at the top end to avoid the need for this correction. For internal curves, a boring tool, set to the cutting radius by the same way, can be employed. It is obviously possible to improve this simple device in many ways, such as by providing a radial tool slide, and a mechanical movement for rotation round the pivot. But as explained above, justification for any such elaboration will depend on individual circumstances.

Contour Turning

This often presents a problem in lathe work, and again the use of form tools is possible in lathes of substantial size and rigidity. But in light lathes, other methods, such as roughing out with slide rest tools and finishing by hand turning, may have to be employed. Where a number of parts, such as the crank extensions of machine tool handles, have to be made, it is not easy to ensure uniformity of shape and dimensions, and examples of very slovenly work, by turners who should know better, are frequently encountered.

It is possible to turn contours which are not too deep by copy turning, adapting a taper turning attachment or equivalent device. The feed screw of the cross slide must be detached, and the slide either spring-loaded or fitted with a weight with a cord running over a pulley at the back of the lathe. A template or master form is attached to the stationary fixture, and a follower fixed to the back end of the cross slide to make contact with it. A roller or small ball race may with advantage be used for this purpose, but the shape of the follower must be allowed for in setting out the contour of the template. Only a very small area, virtually a point contact of the follower, can be used to reproduce the shape of the template with near exactitude, and this is not desirable for mechanical reasons.

Contour turning, including one-way stepped or tapered work, is often carried out industrially by means of hydraulic or other automatic copying devices. These are usually fitted at the back of the lathe, and employ a probe or tracer which moves along the master form (sometimes a sample of the component to be produced), and actuate a pilot valve which controls the motion of a piston in the tool slide. The Minikop lathe made by Myfords, specially for this kind of work, employs hydraulic feed for the sliding saddle as well as for the copying movement. It is capable of producing parts of high precision, at rates comparable to those attainable by capstan and automatic production lathes employing form tools. Attachments for copy turning can be obtained for several types of general-purpose lathes including Colchester and Harrison.

Non-circular Turning

In most lathe operations, circular accuracy is of the highest importance, but there are occasions when it is necessary to produce work which is not of circular cross-section. Generally this is done by co-ordinate milling, but it can be done on the lathe if means are provided for controlled reciprocation of the cutting tool during the rotation of the work. Some early types of lathes were equipped with rocking headstocks or slide rests for this purpose, the motion of which could be controlled by a cam or "rosette" on the mandrel. The same principle is employed at the present day in grinding machines for cams and similar components, but for lathes it is generally more convenient to employ a spring- or weight-loaded

FIG. 11-2: The Myford Minikop lathe for automatic copying from template or sample

slide, as for simple contour turning.

A typical example of non-circular turning occurs in the manufacture of car engine pistons, in which the object is to avoid binding due to uneven expansion in the cross plane of the gudgeon pin. In this instance the deviation from circular amounts to no more than a few thousandths of an inch, but it is possible to turn cams with fairly substantial lift, and even to produce hexagons or other polygonal shapes, in the same way. It is generally necessary to drive the work slowly to avoid errors caused by inertia of the tool slide, and also to increase the front clearance angle of the tool sufficiently to avoid fouling on the rising side of the cam. The tools employed for cam turning are usually "knife" tools, cutting on

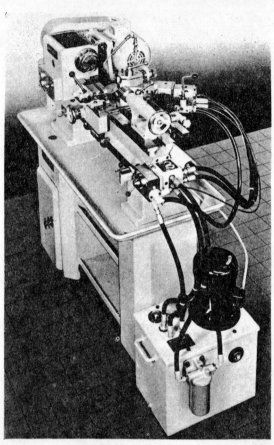

FIG. II–3: End view of Minikop lathe, showing hydraulic equipment

the side, with a fine traversing feed, to full depth at one cut.

The reciprocating movement of the slide is generally obtained by means of a master cam mounted on the live mandrel, or geared to it on a layshaft running in the same direction at the same speed. Similar principles are used when turning blanks for cutters, reamers or taps, for relieving the cutting edges. Special lathes designed for this purpose are equipped with complex movements for edge, side and helical relieving. It is usual to gash the individual flutes or cutting edges by milling, to give clearance for the relieving tool to start or run out into. Cutters for forming the teeth of gears and similar operations employ accurately shaped form tools for both rough turning and relieving, and the cutters produced in this way are said to be "form-relieved".

In the absence of special equipment for relieving, it is possible to relieve *individual* teeth of a cutter blank by mounting it on an eccentric mandrel, and rotating it through a limited angle. It is advisable to use a lever for this operation, with stops set to prevent turning it too far. The individual teeth are indexed in any convenient way in relation to the eccentric mandrel. Although much slower than the use of a reciprocating tool slide, this process needs only the simplest adaptation to the lathe equipment, and produces quite satisfactory results. The machining of convex cam flank contours can also be carried out by turning processes, using an eccentric mounting fixture for the blank, with means of indexing it to the required angles for the flank locations. This method has been found highly satisfactory for forming camshafts of model petrol engines with multiple cams exactly timed.

Spinning

Circular components in ductile metals such as annealed copper, aluminium and steel can be produced by pressing into shape while rotating in the lathe. This process, known as spinning, can be carried out on the simplest lathes, and does not even call for the use of a slide-rest. A pattern or former, of shape and size corresponding to the inside contour of the required object, is first turned in metal or hardwood. A disc of sheet metal, large enough to produce the complete component, is fastened concentrically to the front face of the former. If it is not permissible to pierce the centre of the metal, it can be driven by friction, backed up by a pad against a running tailstock centre.

The lathe is run at a fairly high speed, and the metal is progressively forced into contact with the former by means of a burnishing tool of wood or metal, manipulated by hand and supported by a suitable hand rest. In order to obtain sufficient leverage to deform the metal, the rest is generally provided with a number of holes, into which a peg can be inserted to form a fulcrum for the tool. Hardwood tools are often used for rough shaping, and followed by hardened steel bullnose or ball-ended tools for finishing. Specially shaped tools for beading, grooving and other detail work may be employed. Steel tools should be highly polished so that they cannot score or scrape the metal, which needs to be kept lubricated with tallow, soap or grease.

It is fairly easy to spin shallow shapes such as dishes, or domed ends for pressure vessels, but the operation increases in difficulty as the depth or sharpness of angle at the sides becomes greater. A slight draught angle on the former is advisable to ensure that the work will come away from it easily. Where the shape of the work involves undercuts, such as inturned angles, curves or grooves, this calls for the use of a segmental former which will collapse inwards for removal. If only a single component is required, a solid wooden former can be used, and burnt out afterwards, but this is obviously uneconomical if the operation needs to be repeated.

The burnishing action on the metal tends to work-harden it, and re-annealing may be found necessary several times in the course of a deep spinning operation. Some stretching of the metal generally takes place, but thin sheet metal may tend to crease or pucker up, making smooth finish impossible. Soft metals up to about sixteen gauge or $\frac{1}{16}$ in. in thickness may be spun on a $3\frac{1}{2}$ in. or 4 in. lathe of normal type, but for harder or thicker metal, heavy end and side thrusts are involved, which call for robust mandrel bearings and headstock structure.

In industrial practice, fairly tough steel components are often produced by a process known as "flow turning", which is virtually a combination of deformation by spinning, and normal turning with cutting tools, in a single operation.

Abrasive Finishing

The use of abrasives, such as emery cloth, for finishing work in the lathe, is frequently necessary, though it should always be the aim of the turner to produce as good a tool finish as possible, so that very little subsequent work on it, with mild or fine abrasive media, needs to be done. The term "lapping" applied to this method of finishing, is incorrect, as it is simply scouring or polishing, which contributes nothing to *accurate* surface finish, and may even have the reverse effect. For finishing a shaft journal, the emery cloth, whether applied by hand, buff stick, or a shaped pad, should be kept constantly moving endwise to produce a criss-cross scratch pattern, as distinct from circular scoring, which may look better, but will have inferior wearing quality. Surface finish is of the highest possible importance in mechanical components, and special processes, such as "super-finishing", are often employed, also special instruments to measure the degree of finish obtained, but these are generally outside the scope of ordinary lathe work.

Lapping, in the true sense, defines the particular abrasive process in which the object is to improve flatness, circular and dimensional accuracy. It entails the use of relatively soft metal laps, charged with an abrasive medium, usually suspended in grease, oil or water. The most important lapping materials are carborundum, emery, various silicates, pumice and rouge, in order of lapping efficiency. In charging the lap, particles of the abrasive become embedded in its surface, and act on the material being lapped by rotary, reciprocating or linear movement. The lap should be of softer metal than that on which it operates; for instance, cast iron, charged with diamond dust, can be used to lap the hardest materials known, not excluding the diamond itself. Generally, the softer the metal of the lap, the easier it is charged, and the faster it works; lead laps are efficient for coarse lapping, but not so good for high accuracy and finish, for which copper or aluminium is preferable.

Some wear of the lap necessarily occurs in use, and for internal lapping of bores for cylinders, piston valves or sleeves, a lap which can be adjusted to the size of the bore, such as by splitting and mounting on a taper mandrel, is recommended. Laps in the form of copper sleeves mounted on expanding arbors, are commercially available. Spring laps of any kind cannot be relied upon to produce either circular or dimensional accuracy, though they may produce satisfactory results where tool finish is sufficiently accurate to require little or no correction. External surfaces may be improved by the use of split ring laps, held in a carrier or die holder. Graded lapping with *separate* laps charged with successively finer media, will produce anything up to mirror finish, but this is generally less important than its virtues in producing accuracy.

Honing is comparable to lapping in most respects, and produces similar results, but instead of using the usual form of lap, it is carried out by one or more abrasive stones mounted in a suitable holder which can be mounted in the lathe or other machine spindle. Small, narrow slips of india oilstone or similar solid abrasive material are commonly employed, fitted to a mandrel, in grooves with inclined planes, so that they can be adjusted to the size of the bore. The action of the hones is more rapid than lapping, and they will give longer wear than laps, so they are better suited to industrial requirements. They are often spring-loaded, but have limit stops so that they can work only to pre-set dimensions. In common with laps, working speeds of 150 to 200 r.p.m. are suitable; either the tool or the work can be rotated, as may be the more convenient. Lubrication with special oil, or other lubricant, should be constantly applied, and scrupulous after-cleaning is necessary to remove all traces of abrasive particles left by the lap or hone.

Grinding is sometimes carried out in the lathe with the aid of tool post grinders or similar attachments, but it generally involves a risk of abrasive dust getting in slides and bearings, with destructive results. Machines designed for grinding cylindrical surfaces incorporate special provision for protecting all working parts, besides an exceptionally rigid mounting for the grinding wheel. It is often thought that grinding is inherently a precision process, but this is true only if the machine is made to the highest accuracy, and is properly adjusted, including balancing and dressing of the wheel. For such purposes as truing up hardened lathe centres, or minor operations on work too hard to be turned with cutting tools, grinding may be the only solution to the problem; otherwise this process should be kept as far away from the lathe as possible.

Burnishing is sometimes used to obtain a high finish on metal surfaces without or in combination with abrasive action. It is carried out by means of hardened and polished steel tools of suitable shape, as used in spinning, where it is often an integral part of the process. High tool pressure with ample lubrication is usually essential, though dry burnishing is possible if the tool is kept moving over the surface to avoid scoring or seizure. The pressure required depends on the hardness of the metal and the area of the tool surface. Care must be taken to avoid local deformation of the metal, or alteration of its dimensions, as the metal may tend to "flow" under pressure of the tool. Such parts as clock or instrument pivots are often finished by burnishing, as a complement to the highest possible polishing by fine abrasives.

Knurling

Many parts machined in the lathe need to have a knurled finish, and various tools are available for this purpose. Production lathes often have the knurling tool applied axially, in a pre-set holder similar to a die head, but for general lathe work, it is usually more convenient for it to be applied radially in a holder mounted in a tool post. The most common forms of knurling are straight, spiral and diamond or double-diagonal, but other and more complicated ornamental patterns are possible, and are used on many commercial products, such as instrument handles, propelling pencils, etc.

Knurling wheels are made of hardened steel, and mounted on equally hard pivots in various kinds of holders. In the past, hand-applied holders have been used, but the amount of pressure which can be exerted in this way is very limited, even when levering against the hand rest or other support.

Straight or spiral knurling can be carried out with a single wheel, but for producing the diagonal pattern

FIG. 11–4: A swivelling-head knurling tool for diamond knurling (J & S)

which is most useful for providing a good finger-grip on screws and nuts, the simultaneous application of a pair of spiral or diagonal knurls, of the same hand and helix angle, is most efficient. They may be held in a swivelling head which enables their working pressure to be balanced, and this idea may be extended by mounting two or more pairs of knurls, of different pitch, in a self-centring holder.

The operation of knurling involves incision and displacement of metal rather than cutting; consequently it calls for fairly heavy side pressure on the work. As knurls are not usually in action for very long periods, they do not cause excessive load on normal mandrel bearings, provided that they are properly lubricated. But some form of knurling tools are available which eliminate most of the load on the mandrel, by applying the wheels to the top and bottom of the work, with a balanced contracting action.

Delicate application of the knurling tool in making contact with the work is not helpful; a deliberate approach is necessary to obtain a fairly deep impression at once. As the circumference of the work may not be an exact multiple of the knurling wheel pitch, it may tend to

FIG. 11–6: J. & S. knurling tool in operation

FIG. 11–7: A knurling tool with balanced contracting action by Denford Small Tools Ltd.

produce a double or untidy track instead of an even pattern. This can often be corrected by feeding the tool in deeper, but if not, it may be necessary to wipe out the first impression with a turning tool or file, and start again on a slightly smaller diameter. For this reason, it is often a good policy to allow a little extra length for starting the knurling, and turn it away afterwards. The first contact should be made on a very short length, not more than half the width of the wheel, so that a deep impression can be made quickly. A low or medium speed should be used for starting the operation, but higher speed may then be employed to produce a burnishing effect. Lubrication of the work, and also the knurling wheel pivots, is essential for good results.

FIG. 11–5: A turret head knurling tool with three grades of knurling wheels (J. & S.)

FIG. 11–8: Marlco contracting knurling tool in operation

Knurling should always be carried out to completion, that is, to the full depth of the knurling wheel teeth; if not, it will not look well, and burrs may be raised which could damage the fingers when using the knurled component. Slovenly knurling is all too common, not only among amateurs but also professional turners. The swaging action of a straight (axial) knurl may be applied to serve as a "putting-on tool", as it will raise the surface of a shaft so as to restore the fit of a slightly oversize bore in a wheel or boss. Even if this is not necessary, the keying effect of the serrations is often useful to provide a secure hold of a driven component. In the same way, a knurl held in a special holder may be applied to the inside of a bush or ball race housing to make good an imperfect fit, though this is not recommended as a general practice.

Filing in the Lathe

Most turners employ a file on rotating work at some time or other, though it has often been roundly condemned, and it cannot be con-

sidered as the best practice. It is permissible to use a very fine smooth file to improve finish on occasional work, or to form a slight taper on a mandrel, or perhaps a bush, for easing its entry into a bore. Files are often used to "break" a corner on work, or produce a slight chamfer, but a cutting tool is much to be preferred for either purpose. If a file is used to remove more than a mere thousandth of an inch or so, there is a risk that it may not work evenly, and thus impair the roundness of the surface. Files are also prone to produce scores or scratches, and on some metals they "pin up" badly, and accentuate these faults.

The common practice of using a file to shape contours on handles and similar objects is very inefficient compared with the use of cutting tools, and is definitely to be discouraged. Apart from other objections to filing, it often calls for an awkward position in relation to the lathe, and cases have been known where the operator's sleeve has caught in the carrier or chuck, and caused a more or less serious accident. The general attitude among turners to filing in the lathe is "We all do it, but we don't boast about it!"

Balancing

The rotating parts of the lathe, and the work being machined, should always be as well balanced as possible. Most modern lathes have the mandrel, pulleys and gearing carefully balanced, but much of the work and fixtures mounted in the chuck, or on the faceplate, are offset from the centre or for other reasons are not in natural balance. The effect of unbalance, especially at high speed, is to cause vibration, which is never desirable, and if excessive, may affect accurate machining, besides causing stresses in working parts.

Wherever possible, some attempt should be made to balance the rotating work, at least to the extent that no perceptible vibration is caused at the working speed employed. For faceplate-mounted work, it is generally possible to do this by attaching any suitable pieces of metal such as discs, plates, or collars in positions as near opposite to the offset weight as conditions allow. Static balance, as shown by the mandrel having no tendency to come to rest at one particular position when freed from the belt or other drive, is sufficient in most cases, but if the unbalanced part of the work projects any substantial distance from the faceplate, the balance weight should be located as near as possible to the same *lateral* plane.

For running at the highest speeds, even the unbalanced weight of a driving pin or carrier may have undesirable effects, and correction on the same general principles will be found worth while. Fig. 11–9.

Trepanning

It is often necessary to cut large holes in plates or other work in the

FIG. 11–9: Metal discs attached to face-plate for balancing work and angle plate

lathe. Instead of drilling and boring these out from solid metal, it is often quicker and more efficient to cut them by trepanning or annular machining. A parting tool, set at right angles to the face of the work, is suitable for light operations of this nature, but it must have ample side clearance to avoid fouling the curved sides of the cut, especially in holes of relatively small size. For heavier or more frequent operations, special trepanning tools, which generally include a pilot for centring the cutter from a pre-drilled hole in the work, will be found worth while. They may have two or more radially adjustable cutters to provide a balanced action.

Trepanning of holes is not only an efficient method but is also economical, because the disc of metal removed is not necessarily waste, and may be usable for some other purpose. Conversely, the method may be employed for producing discs from sheet metal. The tools may of course be applied by drilling machines as well as lathes, but for cutting out large holes in tough materials, they call for slow speed and heavy torque for which lathes are generally better suited. In industrial practice, trepanning is often employed for quite deep and heavy machining, using tools similar to hollow milling cutters, with passages to supply coolant and eject chips from the cutting face.

Lubricants and Coolants

The oils and emulsions used in machining serve a dual purpose, in lubricating the cutting tool and also conducting away the heat generated by cutting friction. To some extent these functions are interdependent, but for certain purposes, one may be more important than the other. "Straight" oils, or those with special additives to render them better suited for machining, are obviously the best lubricants, but oil-water emulsions, or "soluble" oils as they are called, conduct heat more efficiently and tend to cooler working in light or moderate machining. These can generally be recommended for a wide variety of materials and operations in which keen and well-set tools are employed; they assist in obtaining high finish and long tool wear.

Oils, and even greases, are better for tapping, die threading and other operations which entail heavy tool loading, but in order to produce efficient cooling they need to be applied continuously and copiously. For heavy screwcutting on alloy steel or other specially tough material, oils or emulsions with additives such as molybdenum disulphide are often helpful. Unless a good deal of fairly heavy work is being done, continuous flooding by means of forced supply is not necessary on general purpose lathes; application by means of a brush or drip can is sufficient for most operations.

Some turners prefer to use lubricants very sparingly, if at all, and prefer to machine work "dry" wherever possible. The object in many cases is to facilitate observation of the work, but sometimes the use of soluble oils is avoided on the grounds that they are liable to produce rust or corrosion of the lathe surfaces. This is largely a fallacy, because with good emulsions, the oil content adheres to the surfaces while the water evaporates away. But this assumes that the compound is free of acids or other active chemicals, and that the workshop is not subject to excess humidity or rapid changes of temperature, which would inevitably cause rusting in any case. If any machine working surface should show signs of beginning to rust, the visible film should not be scoured away, by emery cloth or other abrasive, but coated with an anti-rust oil which will prevent it going any deeper. If machines are laid up for any length of time, it is prudent to spray the surfaces with a special rust preventative such as Shell Ensis oil, which partially dries out to leave a tenacious residue, easily removable when necessary by a light solvent such as paraffin or petrol.

In workshops attached or adjacent to domestic buildings, the use of cutting lubricants is often objected to by reason of their smell. This may be pervasive and not very pleasant in some cases, but it has been given special consideration by oil manufacturers in recent years. The same applies to the irritant effect of these preparations on the skin, and many of them, including the Shell Dromus soluble oils now have antiseptic and deodorant properties. But oils, when used on operations which generate considerable heat, are liable to decompose, and produce smells comparable with that of bad cooking, which are difficult to suppress or eradicate. If for no other reason than this, it is a good policy to avoid high temperatures in machining operations.

CHAPTER 12

MEASUREMENT, MARKING-OUT AND TESTING

IN order to produce work of high quality and accuracy on the lathe, it is necessary to make good use of measuring instruments. These may broadly be divided into two classes, namely, comparators, and those which give absolute dimensions. In the former class are calipers of various kinds which do not incorporate a graduated scale, and in the latter, scale rulers, slide calipers, depth gauges and micrometers. Full details of all kinds of measuring instruments cannot be given in this book, but they are fully dealt with in the companion handbook *Micrometers, Slide Gauges and Calipers.*

For internal and external measurement of turned work, to moderately close limits, quite simple instruments are adequate if reasonable skill and care are exercised in their use. The most popular instruments for comparative measurements are calipers of the firm joint or spring bow type. While the latter have better facility of adjustment, the firm joint type is often preferred because of its greater rigidity. But both types have a certain degree of elasticity and can be sprung over a diameter, or into a bore, several thousandths of an inch over or under the size to which they are set. To obtain maximum accuracy with calipers, they must be set and applied with the utmost delicacy, using the sense of touch to judge their friction in contact with the work.

To set calipers as close as possible to any required dimension, it is helpful to have available a gauge, or a sample piece of material of the specified size to which they can be applied. By comparison between the "feel" on the gauge piece against that on the work, it is possible to work to limits of two or three thousandths of an ·inch with care and skill. Less accurate, but still useful approximate measurements can be obtained by setting the calipers against a steel rule as shown in Fig. 12–1. If a slide gauge with inside and outside jaws is available, highly accurate setting of calipers for either measurement is possible. For small internal dimensions, calipers can be set from a micrometer measurement.

FIG. 12–1: Setting outside or inside calipers to dimensions on a steel rule

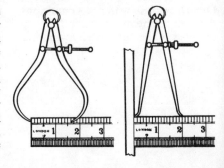

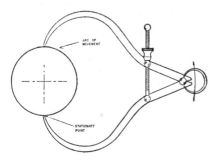

FIG. 12-2: Method of using outside calipers

When applying outside calipers to turned work, they should be held near the pivot point between the thumb and finger so that they are free to centre themselves, with equal friction on each contact point, and squarely across the work axis. For fine feel, one point may then be held steady while the other is rocked over the maximum diameter, as shown in Fig. 12-2. Oversize error is indicated by excessive friction of the moving contact point or its refusal to pass over the work. For the finest limit of accuracy, it should have very little frictional resistance, and touch the work at a mere point.

Inside calipers are held in a similar way, but presented axially to the work, with the contact points across the axis of the bore. They are rocked both from the joint, and crosswise, to ensure that the measurement is taken across the maximum diameter. The amount of cross

FIG. 12-3: Method of using inside calipers

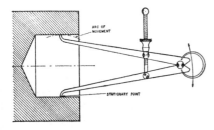

movement possible, without encountering appreciable resistance, gives the most accurate indication of internal diameter. Fig. 12-3.

It need hardly be added that the work should be stationary when applying calipers, or indeed any other measuring instruments. Sometimes calipers are applied to rotating work when it is nearing finished size, to judge how much further it needs to be reduced, but apart from causing wear and burring of the contact points, there is a risk that they may be caught by the work and more seriously damaged.

The most useful instrument for precision measurement is the micrometer in any of its various forms. Many turners would consider that an outside micrometer, at least, is indispensable for lathe work. The size reading from 0 to 1 in. will cover a wide range of ordinary requirements, but larger sizes often have to be measured, and where economy is a prime consideration, greater scope is obtained by a larger micrometer with interchangeable anvils to enable it to be adapted for the smaller size ranges. The handiness and compactness of the little one-inch "mike", however, enables it to be carried in the pocket, and it is the constant companion of many a skilled fitter and turner, whether amateur or professional.

Simple but well-made micrometers without frills are obtainable at quite moderate prices, but the buyer should beware of very cheap instruments *miscalled* micrometers, which are often useless for serious measurement. Some of these have zinc alloy die cast bodies, and apart from any other faults, the metal is liable to distortion in course of time, which would affect accuracy of calibration. Good quality micrometers have steel or cast iron bows, heat treated to ensure stability. Refinements such as ratchet or friction stops to ensure constant feel on the work, or spindle locks which do not affect setting, are well worth their extra cost. Special anvils for measurement of screw threads and similar purposes can be fitted to standard micrometers.

The normal scale of a decimal-inch micrometer reads to 1/1,000 in. but by the addition of a vernier scale, it can be read to finer limits, down to 1/10,000 in. Metric micrometers are normally graduated to 1/100 mm. It is now possible to obtain micrometers with a double scale to read both decimal-inch and metric measurements. It is generally easier to attain accuracy by means of a micrometer than with any other instrument, because apart from other merits, it will indicate the exact amount of oversize or undersize error.

Micrometers for internal measurement are less commonly used than the external type, as it is generally more convenient to use gauges, or rely on standard sizing tools. For the larger sizes of holes, direct-reading micrometers are available, and can be fitted with extension spindles in ½ in. or 1 in. increments of length to cover a wide range of dimensions. Smaller

holes can be measured by indirect-reading micrometers in which balls or other contacts are employed in conjunction with a micrometer head or a dial test indicator.

Slide gauges with vernier scales for fractional-inch and metric measurements can be obtained in various sizes, and in some cases will give simultaneous external, internal and depth readings to very fine limits. This is a great advantage when machining parts which have to fit together, though they are less convenient for direct application to lathe work than calipers or micrometers. Depth gauges, such as shown in Fig. 12–7, are very useful, not only for use in holes and recesses, but also for external application, measuring height from base, length of a step, or a shouldered shaft. For precision work, a micrometer depth gauge such as that shown in Fig. 12–8, is recommended. Other forms of direct-reading scaled instruments such as the vernier height gauges, have their

FIG. 12–4: The Moore & Wright 1 in. micrometer

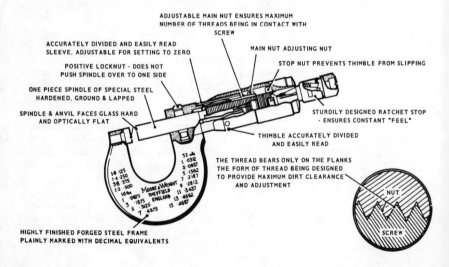

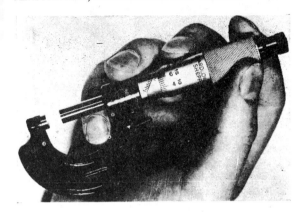

FIG. 12–5: Shardlow micrometer for simultaneous decimal–inch and metric measurements

uses in lathe work, but are less essential than those mentioned.

For precision testing of concentricity and alignment, also many other applications, dial test indicators are so useful that they are often regarded as indispensable. The simpler forms of these instruments employ a simple or compound lever system to magnify the movement of the contact point. More elaborate types have a straight-line plunger movement, with multiplying gears to actuate the dial pointer. Most of them are designed for external application, but can be fitted with an extension for use inside holes; they can be mounted in a holder fitted

to the lathe tool post, or to other machine tool fixtures.

One of the handiest dial test indicators is the Verdict, which is small and compact, and can be used with equal facility on either external or internal surfaces. The contact point can be set at various angles, and its action is reversible, so that the dial will read in either direction. It is equipped with a swivelling holder for fitting to the tool post, or the pillar of a surface gauge; a magnetic base can also be obtained, which will adhere firmly to any cast iron or steel surface. Among many less obvious applications of dial indicators, they may be fitted to machine slides to indicate limits of travel, and to serve as comparators in various inspection and checking operations. Even if the accuracy of the cheaper instruments and their calibration throughout the full range of dial movement cannot be guaranteed, they are none the less useful for this purpose.

Bevel gauges and protractors are used for checking angles in setting up work, taper turning and similar operations. For the utmost accuracy in angular measurement, sine bars are generally employed, but it is difficult to apply these directly to

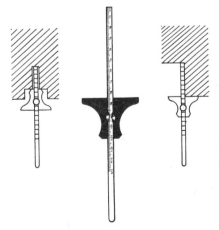

FIG. 12–7: Moore & Wright Depth gauge

FIG. 12–6: Moore &
Wright ball contact
internal micrometer for
small holes

lathe work, and sufficiently high precision is usually obtainable by means of simpler forms of angle gauges. Rake and clearance angles of tools, including those for cutting threads with steep helix angles, can be measured with the device known as a "toolmaker's square", but which is really a limited-angle protractor designed for working in confined spaces. A simpler device, known as a "rake gauge", was formerly obtainable, but is apparently no longer in production; it would not, however, be difficult to make from carbon steel gauge plate.

Marking-out of components, to indicate the position of machined surfaces or bored holes, is a necessary corollary to lathe work in many cases, but the subject is specialised and largely outside the scope of this book. Modern practice tends towards simplifying or reducing the amount of elaborate marking out, in favour of working to co-ordinate measurements from a main datum or reference surface. It is sometimes convenient to carry out simple marking-out on cylindrical work or disc faces while it is set up in the

lathe, such as for marking cross lines exactly across the true diameter, and if necessary extending them along the length. Myford's supply a small surface plate which is designed to be laid on the lathe bed, so that a scribing block, surface gauge or height gauge can be applied for marking-out. If, in addition, a simple means of indexing the lathe mandrel (such as by the use of change wheels) is contrived, equally spaced angles can be marked out on the work, and

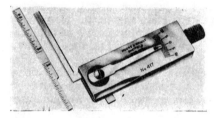

FIG. 12–10: Moore & Wright Tool-maker's Square

FIG. 12–8: Moore & Wright micrometer depth gauge

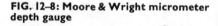

FIG. 12–9:
Section of
Verdict dial
test indicator

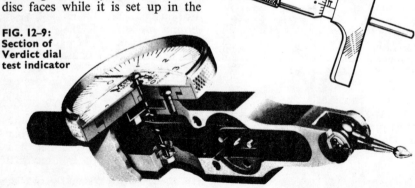

FIG. 12–11: Use of Myford surface plate for marking-out work in the lathe

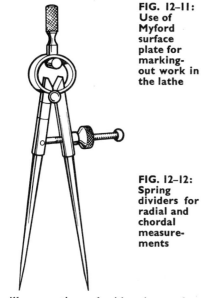

FIG. 12–12: Spring dividers for radial and chordal measurements

will save time, besides improving accuracy, in subsequent operations which may be necessary. Dividers such as shown in Fig. 12–12 are essential in marking-out many radial, diametric and chordal distances; they are, of course, comparators, and usually must be set by means of a rule or other visible scale, but devices are now available for setting them to more precise limits. The same applies to odd-leg or "jenny" calipers, often wrongly referred to as "hermaphro-dite" calipers, though these are really instruments for simultaneous external and internal measurement, now virtually obsolete.

For setting work to run concentrically from a punched or drilled centre-mark, visual observation, even with the aid of a lens, is often inadequate, and various aids to accuracy have been devised. One of the simplest of these is known as a "wobbler" for want of a more technical title; it is not commercially available, but is not difficult to make. Essentially, it consists of a ball-socketed lever with arms of different lengths, mounted in a holder in the tool post. After setting the work to run as truly as possible by eye, the point of the short arm is entered in the indentation, and when the work is rotated, the concentric error will be multiplied at the end of the long arm. To assist visual observation, the tailstock centre may be set fairly close to the point of the arm. Fig. 12–13.

Toolmakers' Buttons

For accurate location of bored holes or turned spigots, either in relation to each other, or to pre-determined surfaces, these are often found useful. They were formerly regarded as indispensable for jig and tool work, but in well-equipped tool rooms, the availability of precision jig boring machines enables them to be dispensed with. The buttons are short steel bushes, precision ground on the diameter and end faces, and hardened, which can be attached to the face of the work by screws and washers so as to allow some latitude of movement. Fig. 12–15.

The required locations are marked out fairly closely by measurement, which may entail co-ordinates from the sides and ends of the workpiece. At the required points, holes are drilled and tapped for the holding screws, and before these are fully tightened, the buttons are adjusted to the *exact* positions, using a slide

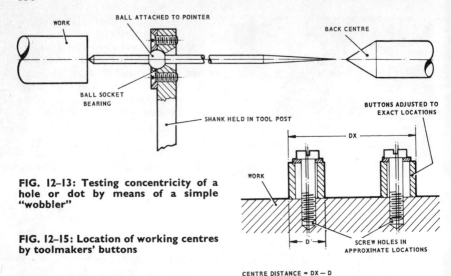

FIG. 12–13: Testing concentricity of a hole or dot by means of a simple "wobbler"

FIG. 12–15: Location of working centres by toolmakers' buttons

CENTRE DISTANCE = DX − D

gauge, micrometer or depth gauge as may be most convenient. In the example shown it is required to locate two holes at an exact distance from each other; the essential measurement is taken over the outside of the buttons, or between their

FIG. 12–14: Checking parallel accuracy of work machines between centres on Boxford lathe

inside surfaces, with allowance for their known diameter in either case. The work is then set up in the lathe, and each of the buttons adjusted in turn to run truly with the aid of a dial test indicator, prior to removing them and boring out the holes to the specified size. The complete process may seem tedious, especially if a number of locations is involved, but it may be the only means of ensuring

accuracy in the absence of special machine tool facilities.

Alignment tests of Lathes

In order to test the accuracy of a lathe, it should first be ascertained that the bearings and slides are in proper working order and adjusted to minimum working clearance. No test can be valid if any of the mechanical movements are rough, slack or erratic. The first and most important test is to ensure that the mandrel axis is in exact parallel alignment with the sliding ways of the bed. Lathe makers can usually supply or loan a parallel test bar which can be fitted to the mandrel socket for this purpose. If the taper of the latter is concentric, smooth, and of correct angle, the bar will run quite truly. If not, steps should be taken to correct running error.

With the bar running truly, a check for parallelism of the bed slides can be made along its length, preferably by means of a dial test indicator mounted in the tool post. Deviation of the pointer, as the slide is moved lengthwise, is a definite indication of error, which is usually most easily corrected by adjusting the position of the complete headstock. In some lathes, fine adjustment screws are fitted to its base for this purpose, and only a very slight movement is necessary to effect perfect alignment. If a test bar is not available, a piece of material may be held in the chuck, and a fine test cut taken along it by the saddle traversing movement. Measurements taken by micrometer or calipers at extreme ends of the cut should coincide within very close limits. Intermediate measurements are not normally necessary, but if they should show any discrepancy, it indicates that something is radically wrong with the sliding movement.

The alignment on the vertical axis should also be checked, as wear of mandrel bearings, even after refitting, may cause the mandrel to droop at the nose end. Lathes in which the headstock is cast integral with the bed may call for more drastic methods of correcting error, such as by scraping the bearings or the sliding ways of the bed.

The squareness of the cross slide with the lathe axis may be tested by taking a fine cut across the surface of a large disc held in the chuck. Normally the cross slideways are integral with the saddle, and concave or convex area can only be corrected by scraping either these ways, or those of the saddle itself. The alignment of the tailstock, both in the vertical and horizontal planes, can easily be checked by inserting the centres in both sockets and bringing them together with a thin piece of metal between them. If it tilts in either direction, error is indicated, assuming that the centres are both true and correctly pointed. This test does not prove that the tailstock barrel is truly in parallel alignment with the bed, but this can be checked by using a socketed test bar, as for the live mandrel. Other tests which can be carried out include those for true running of faceplates, chucks or adaptors. It is of course essential that the register, and the face of the shoulder on the mandrel nose, should be beyond reproach in this respect. Slight wobble on the face of screwed fittings can usually be corrected by discreet local scraping of the back locating surface.

Lathe users, other than those with practical experience of machine tool fitting, are strongly advised not to attempt any drastic alterations which might permanently affect the accuracy of a lathe. It is safer to accept the minor inaccuracies of the machine, and learn to live with them.

Even the most expensive lathe cannot be expected to remain in perfect adjustment indefinitely, and all machines have their limitations. Those who expect a machine to turn out perfect work automatically, often in spite of careless handling and abuse, are liable to be sadly disappointed.

APPENDICES

I. Screwcutting Tables.
Myford ML7 and Super 7 (8 T.P.I. Lead Screw).

II. Drummond Round Bed (10 T.P.I. Lead Screw).

III. Metric and Decimal Equivalents of fractions of an inch.

IV. Tables of Threads (Whit., B.S.F. and B.A.).
M.E. Fine Threads.
Unified Threads (UNC and UNF).

V. Circumferences and Areas of Circles.

VI. Draw-in Collets.

VII. Standard Taper Shanks and Sockets.

VIII. Recommended Lubricants.

IX. Surface Speeds for machining metals.

I.

SCREWCUTTING TABLES
MYFORD ML7 AND SUPER 7 LATHES

(8 T.P.I. Lead Screw)*

T.P.I.	Feed per Rev.	Driver	1st Stud		2nd Stud		Lead-screw
			Driven	Driver	Driven	Driver	
8	0·1250"	35	20	40	Idle Wheel		70
9	0·1111"	40	Idle Wheel		,, ,,		45
10	0·1000"	40	,, ,,		,, ,,		50
11	0·0909"	40	,, ,,		,, ,,		55
12	0·0833"	40	,, ,,		,, ,,		60
14	0·0714"	20	,, ,,		,, ,,		35
16	0·0625"	20	,, ,,		,, ,,		40
18	0·0556"	20	,, ,,		,, ,,		45
19	0·0526"	40	38	20	Idle Wheel		50
20	0·0500"	20	Idle Wheel		,, ,,		50
22	0·0455"	20	,, ,,		,, ,,		55
24	0·0417"	20	,, ,,		,, ,,		60
25	0·0400"	20	25	20	Idle Wheel		50
26	0·0385"	20	Idle Wheel		Idle Wheel		65
28	0·0357"	30	35	20	Idle Wheel		60
32	0·0313"	30	40	20	,, ,,		60
36	0·0278"	30	45	20	,, ,,		60
40	0·0250"	30	50	20	,, ,,		60
44	0·0227"	20	55	30	,, ,,		60
46	0·0217"	20	46	30	,, ,,		75
48	0·0208"	20	60	35	,, ,,		70
52	0·0192"	20	50	25	,, ,,		65
54	0·0185"	20	45	20	,, ,,		60
60	0·0167"	20	50	25	,, ,,		75
64	0·0156"	20	50	25	40	30	60
72	0·0139"	20	40	30	45	20	60
80	0·0125"	20	40	30	50	20	60
88	0·0114"	20	40	25	55	30	75
92	0·0109"	20	46	30	50	20	60
96	0·0104"	20	40	25	50	20	60
104	0·0096"	20	40	20	50	25	65
	0·0087"	20	55	30	60	25	65
112	0·0089"	25	50	30	60	20	70
120	0·0083"	20	40	20	50	25	75
	0·0058"	20	55	25	60	20	65
	0·0043"	20	60	25	65	20	75
	0·0037"	20	65	25	70	20	75
	0·0025"	20	70	25	75	20	95

Self-Acting Feeds { 104, 112, 120 ... }

METRIC PITCHES

T.P.I.	Feed per Rev.	Driver	1st Stud		2nd Stud		Lead-screw
	0·50 mm	20	60	65	50	20	55
	0·75	30	60	65	50	20	55
	1·00	65	30	20	50	20	55
	1·25	20	60	65	Idle Wheel		55
	1·50	20	55	65	,, ,,		50
	1·75	30	60	55	,, ,,		50
	2·00	20	50	55	,, ,,		35
	2·25	30	55	65	,, ,,		50
	2·50	40	60	65	,, ,,		55
	2·75	40	60	65	,, ,,		50
	3·00	40	50	65	,, ,,		55

*Applicable to other lathes with 8 T.P.I. lead screw, provided that suitable change wheels are available.

II.   SCREWCUTTING TABLES

"A" Type 4″ Round Bed Drummond Lathe
(10 T.P.I. Lead Screw)

Change Wheels, Standard Set
2 each 20 and 40 tooth.
1 each 25, 26, 30, 35, 45, 50 and 66 tooth.

Threads per inch	Mandrel	Driven on Stud	Driver on Stud	Lead Screw
5	50	—	—	25
6	50	—	—	30
7	50	—	—	35
8	50	—	—	40
9	50	—	—	45
10	40	—	—	40
11	30	20	40	66
12	25	—	—	30
13	20	—	—	26
14	25	—	—	35
16	25	—	—	40
18	25	—	—	45
20	25	—	—	50
24	25	40	20	30
26	20	26	20	40
28	25	40	20	35
32	25	40	20	40
36	25	40	20	45
40	25	40	20	50

Fine Feeds

Cuts per inch	Mandrel	Driven on Reverse Stud	Driver on Reverse Stud	Driven on 1st Stud	Driver on 1st Stud	Driven on 2nd Stud	Driver on 2nd Stud	Lead Screw
148·5	20	—	—	45	25	50	20	66
200	20	35	26	45	25	50	20	66

Metric Threads

Pitch, m/m	Mandrel	Driven on Stud	Driver on Stud	Lead Screw
0·50	26	40	20	66
0·75	26	40	30	66
1·00	26	—	—	66
1·25	26	40	50	66
1·50	26	20	30	66
1·75	26	20	35	66
2·00	26	20	40	66
2·25	26	20	45	66
2·50	50	20	26	66

III. METRIC AND DECIMAL EQUIVALENTS OF FRACTIONS OF AN INCH

Inches		m/m	Inches		m/m
1/64	·015	0·396	33/64	·516	13·096
1/32	·031	0·793	17/32	·531	13·492
3/64	·047	1·190	35/64	·547	13·890
1/16	·063	1·587	9/16	·563	14·267
5/64	·078	1·984	37/64	·578	14·683
3/32	·094	2·381	19/32	·594	15·080
7/64	·109	2·778	39/64	·609	15·477
1/8	·125	3·175	5/8	·625	15·875
9/64	·141	3·571	41/64	·641	16·271
5/32	·156	3·968	21/32	·656	16·667
11/64	·172	4·365	43/64	·672	17·064
3/16	·188	4·762	11/16	·688	17·462
13/64	·203	5·159	45/64	·703	17·858
7/32	·219	5·556	23/32	·719	18·255
15/64	·234	5·952	47/64	·734	18·652
1/4	·25	6·350	3/4	·75	19·050
17/64	·266	6·746	49/64	·766	19·446
9/32	·281	7·143	25/32	·781	19·842
19/64	·297	7·540	51/64	·797	20·239
5/16	·313	7·937	13/16	·813	20·637
21/64	·328	8·334	53/64	·828	21·033
11/32	·344	8·730	27/32	·844	21·429
23/64	·359	9·127	55/64	·859	21·827
3/8	·375	9·525	7/8	·875	22·225
25/64	·391	9·921	57/64	·891	22·621
13/32	·406	10·318	29/32	·906	23·017
27/64	·422	10·715	59/64	·922	23·414
7/16	·438	11·112	15/16	·938	23·812
29/64	·453	11·508	61/64	·953	24·208
15/32	·469	11·905	31/32	·969	24·604
31/64	·404	12·302	63/64	·984	25·002
1/2	·5	12·700	1	1·0	25·4

IV.   THREAD TABLES

B.S. Whitworth Threads

Dia.	Tapping	Clearance	Threads per in.
1/16	No. 56	No. 52	60
3/32	No. 49	No. 41	48
1/8	No. 38	No. 30	40
5/32	No. 30	No. 21	32
3/16	No. 25	No. 11	24
7/32	No. 15	No. 2	24
1/4	No. 6	Letter F	20
5/16	Letter G	Letter P	20
3/8	Letter O	Letter W	16
7/16	3/8	29/64	14
1/2	27/64	33/64	12
9/16	31/64	37/64	12
5/8	35/64	41/64	11
3/4	21/32	49/64	10
7/8	49/64	57/64	9
1 in.	7/8	1-1/64	8

B.S. Fine Threads

Dia.	Tapping	Clearance	Threads per in.
3/16	No. 22	No. 11	32
7/32	No. 13	No. 2	28
1/4	No. 3	Letter F	26
9/32	Letter C	Letter L	26
5/16	Letter I	Letter P	22
3/8	21/64	Letter W	20
7/16	Letter W	29/64	18
1/2	7/16	33/64	16
9/16	1/2	37/64	16
5/8	9/16	41/64	14
11/16	5/8	45/64	14
3/4	43/64	49/64	12
13/16	47/64	53/64	12
7/8	51/64	57/64	11
1 in.	29/32	1-1/64	10

B.A. Threads

Dia.	Tapping	Clearance	Threads (m/m)
0	No. 8	Letter B	1·00
1	No. 16	No. 3	1·90
2	No. 22	No. 12	0·81
3	No. 29	No. 19	0·73
4	No. 32	No. 27	0·66
5	No. 36	No. 30	0·59
6	No. 42	No. 33	0·53
7	No. 45	No. 38	0·48
8	No. 50	No. 43	0·43
9	No. 53	No. 47	0·39
10	No. 54	No. 50	0·35
11	No. 56	No. 53	0·31
12	No. 58	No. 55	0·28

M.E. (Model Engineer) Threads

Dia.	Tapping	Clearance	Threads per in.
1/8	No. 38	No. 29	40
5/32	No. 30	No. 19	40
3/16	No. 20	No. 9	40
7/32	No. 9	No. 1	40
1/4	No. 1	Letter G	40
9/32	Letter E	Letter M	32
5/16	9/32	Letter P	32
3/8	11/32	Letter W	32
7/16	Letter X	29/64	26
1/2	15/32	33/64	26

All dimensions are in inches.

Unified Thread Series

Size	UN Coarse (UNC) (T.P.I.)	UN Fine (UNF) (T.P.I.)
1/4	20	28
5/16	18	24
3/8	14	24
7/16	14	20
1/2	13	20
9/16	12	18
5/8	11	18
3/4	10	16
7/8	9	14
1	8	12
1-1/8	7	12
1-1/4	7	12
1-3/8	6	12
1-1/2	6	12

V. CIRCUMFERENCES AND AREAS OF CIRCLES

Diameter	Circumference	Area
1/64	0.0491	0.00019
1/32	0.0982	0.00077
3/64	0.1473	0.00173
1/16	0.1964	0.00307
3/32	0.2945	0.00690
1/8	0.3927	0.01227
5/32	0.4809	0.01917
3/16	0.5890	0.02761
7/32	0.6872	0.03758
1/4	0.7854	0.04909
9/32	0.8836	0.06213
5/16	0.9817	0.07679
11/32	1.0799	0.09281
3/8	1.1781	0.11045
13/32	1.2763	0.12962
7/16	1.3745	0.15033
15/32	1.4726	0.17257
1/2	1.5708	0.19635
17/32	1.6690	0.22166
9/16	1.7672	0.24850
19/32	1.8653	0.27688
5/8	1.9635	0.30680
21/32	2.0617	0.33824
11/16	2.1598	0.37122
23/32	2.2580	0.40574
3/4	2.3562	0.44179
25/32	2.4544	0.47947
13/16	2.5525	0.51849
27/32	2.6507	0.55914
7/8	2.7489	0.60132
29/32	2.8471	0.65404
15/16	2.9452	0.69029
31/32	3.0434	0.73708

Diameter	Circumference	Area
1	3.1416	0.78540
1 1/16	3.3379	0.88664
1 1/8	3.5343	0.99402
1 3/16	3.7306	1.1075
1 1/4	3.9270	1.2272
1 3/8	4.1233	1.3530
1 7/16	4.3197	1.4849
1 1/2	4.5160	1.6230
1 9/16	4.7124	1.7671
1 5/8	4.9087	1.9175
1 11/16	5.1051	2.0739
1 3/4	5.3014	2.2365
1 13/16	5.4978	2.4053
1 7/8	5.6941	2.5802
1 15/16	5.8905	2.7612
2	6.0868	2.9483
2 1/16	6.2832	3.1416
2 1/8	6.4795	3.3466
2 3/16	6.6759	3.5466
2 1/4	6.8722	3.7583
2 5/16	7.0686	3.9761
2 3/8	7.2649	4.2000
2 7/16	7.4613	4.4301
2 1/2	7.6576	4.6664
2 9/16	7.8540	4.9067
2 5/8	8.0503	5.1572
2 11/16	8.2467	5.4119
2 3/4	8.4430	5.6727
2 13/16	8.6494	5.9396
2 7/8	8.8357	6.2126
2 15/16	9.0321	6.4918
3	9.2284	6.7771

Diameter	Circumference	Area
3	9.4248	7.0686
3 1/16	9.6211	7.3662
3 1/8	9.8175	7.6699
3 3/16	10.0138	7.9798
3 1/4	10.2102	8.2958
3 5/16	10.4065	8.6179
3 3/8	10.6029	8.9462
3 7/16	10.7992	9.2806
3 1/2	10.9956	9.6211
3 9/16	11.1919	9.9678
3 5/8	11.3883	10.321
3 11/16	11.5846	10.680
3 3/4	11.7810	11.045
3 13/16	11.9773	11.416
3 7/8	12.1737	11.793
3 15/16	12.3700	12.177
4	12.5664	12.566
4 1/16	12.7627	12.962
4 1/8	12.9591	13.364
4 3/16	13.1554	13.772
4 1/4	13.3518	14.186
4 5/16	13.5481	14.607
4 3/8	13.7445	15.033
4 7/16	13.9408	15.466
4 1/2	14.1372	15.904
4 9/16	14.3335	16.349
4 5/8	14.5299	16.800
4 11/16	14.7262	17.257
4 3/4	14.9226	17.721
4 13/16	15.1189	18.190
4 7/8	15.3153	18.665
4 15/16	15.5116	19.147

Diameter	Circumference	Area
5	15.7080	19.635
5 1/16	15.9043	20.129
5 1/8	16.1007	20.629
5 3/16	16.2970	21.135
5 1/4	16.4934	21.648
5 5/16	16.6897	22.166
5 3/8	16.8861	22.691
5 7/16	17.0824	23.221
5 1/2	17.2788	23.758
5 9/16	17.4751	24.301
5 5/8	17.6715	24.850
5 11/16	17.8678	25.406
5 3/4	18.0642	25.967
5 13/16	18.2605	26.535
5 7/8	18.4569	27.109
5 15/16	18.6532	27.688
6	18.8496	28.274
6 1/8	19.2423	29.465
6 1/4	19.6350	30.680
6 3/8	20.0277	31.919
6 1/2	20.4204	33.183
6 5/8	20.8131	34.472
6 3/4	21.2058	35.785
6 7/8	21.5984	37.122
7	21.9911	38.485
7 1/8	22.3838	39.871
7 1/4	22.7765	41.282
7 3/8	23.1692	42.718
7 1/2	23.5619	44.179
7 5/8	23.9546	45.664
7 3/4	24.3473	47.173
7 7/8	24.7400	48.707

Diameter	Circumference	Area
8	25.1327	50.265
8 1/8	25.5254	51.849
8 1/4	25.9181	53.456
8 3/8	26.3108	55.088
8 1/2	26.7035	56.745
8 5/8	27.0962	58.426
8 3/4	27.4889	60.132
8 7/8	27.8816	61.862
9	28.2743	63.617
9 1/8	28.6670	65.397
9 1/4	29.0597	67.201
9 3/8	29.4524	69.029
9 1/2	29.8451	70.882
9 5/8	30.2378	72.760
9 3/4	30.6305	74.662
9 7/8	31.0232	76.589
10	31.4159	78.540
10 1/8	31.8086	80.516
10 1/4	32.2013	82.516
10 3/8	32.5940	84.541
10 1/2	32.9867	86.590
10 5/8	33.3794	88.664
10 3/4	33.7721	90.763
10 7/8	34.1648	92.886
11	34.5575	95.033
11 1/8	34.9502	97.205
11 1/4	35.3429	99.402
11 3/8	35.7356	101.42
11 1/2	36.1283	103.87
11 5/8	36.5210	106.14
11 3/4	36.9137	108.43
11 7/8	37.3064	110.75
12	37.6991	113.10

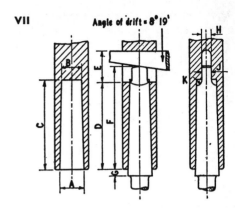

VII   Angle of drift = 8° 19'

VI.   DRAW-IN COLLETS

A	B	C	D	E	F	G (max.)*	H	J	K	L
6	17	30·5	7	5×0·70	10·3	5·0	2·8	40°	8·5	1×0·5
6·5	18·5	32	8	5·6×40 t.p.i.	10·3	5·5	3·2	40°	12	1·5×0'5
8	19·5	36·5	9	6·875×40 t.p.i.	13	7·2	4·5	40°	11	2·0×0·8
10	24	45	11	10×0·85	15	8·0	6·0	40°	14	2·0×0·8
12	31	51	11·5	12×1·0	18	10·0	9·0	40°	16	2·7×0·7
15 (short)	32·5	55·5	12	13×1·0	22	12·7	9·5	40°	16	2·5×0·7
15 (long)	54	83·5	17	13×1·0	22	12·7	9·5	40°	30	2·5×0·7
16	71	110	24·5	14·5×1·20	24	13·0	10·0	40°	28	2·5×1·5

(*This is the largest diameter to which the collet nose can be bored. The largest diameter of rod admitted through the body is limited by dimension H.)
All dimensions are in millimetres, except the thread pitches in the 2nd and 3rd examples.

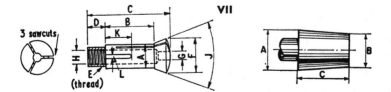

VII. STANDARD TAPER SHANKS AND SOCKETS

Morse Tapers

Taper No.	0	1	2	3	4
A	0·3561	0·475	0 700	0·938	1·231
B	0·252	0·369	0·572	0·778	1·020
C	2	2-1/8	2-9/16	3-3/16	4-1/16
D	1-15/16	2-1/16	2-1/2	3-1/16	3-7/8
E	9/16	3/4	7/8	1-3/16	1-1/4
F	2-7/16	2-7/16	2-15/16	3-11/16	4-5/8
G	1/8	1/8	3/16	3/16	1/4
H	0·160	0·213	0·280	0·322	0·478
J	5/32	13/64	1/4	5/16	15/32
K	5/32	3/16	1/4	9/32	5/16
Taper per ft.	0·625	0·599	0·599	0·602	0·623

Brown & Sharpe Tapers   Taper approx. 1/2″ per foot

Taper No.	A	B	C	D	E	F	G	H	J
1	0·239	0·200	15/16	15/16	3/8	1-3/16	3/32	0·135	1/8
2	0·299	0·250	1-3/16	1-11/64	1/2	1-1/2	3/32	0·166	5/32
3	0·375	0·312	1-1/2	1-15/32	5/8	1-7/8	3/32	0·197	3/16
3	0·385	0·312	1-3/4	1-23/32	5/8	2-1/8	3/32	0·197	3/16
3	0·395	0·312	2	1-31/32	5/8	2-3/8	3/32	0·197	3/16
4	0·402	0·350	1-1/4	1-13/16	11/16	1-21/32	3/32	0·228	7/32
4	0·420	0·350	1-11/16	1-14/64	11/16	2-3/32	3/32	0·228	7/32
5	0·523	0·450	1-3/4	1-11/16	3/4	2-3/16	3/32	0·260	1/4
5	0·533	0·450	2	1-15/16	3/4	2-7/16	3/32	0·260	1/4
5	0·539	0·450	2-1/8	2-1/16	3/4	2-9/16	3/32	0·260	1/4
6	0·599	0·500	2-3/8	2-19/64	7/8	2-7/8	3/32	0·291	9/32
6	0·635	0·500	3-1/4	3-11/64	7/8	3-3/4	3/32	0·291	9/32
7	0·725	0·600	3	2-29/32	15/16	3-17/32	3/32	0·322	5/16
8	0·898	0·750	3-9/16	3-29/64	1	4-1/8	1/8	0·353	11/32
8	0·917	0·750	4	3-57/64	1	4-9/16	1/8	0·353	11/32
9	1·067	0·900	4	3-7/8	1-1/8	4-5/8	1/8	0·385	3/8
9	1·077	0·900	4-1/4	4-1/8	1-1/8	4-7/8	1/8	0·385	3/8

All dimensions are in inches.

Jacobs Tapers

Taper Series	A	B	C	Taper per ft.	Usual Chuck Capacities for Different Series Nos.:
No. 0	0·2500	0·22844	0·43750	0·59145	No. 0 Taper. Drill diameters 0–5/32″
No. 1	0·3840	0·33341	0·65625	0·92508	No. 1 ,, ,, ,, 0–1/4″
No. 2	0·5590	0·48764	0·87500	0·97861	No. 2 ,, ,, ,, 0–3/8″
No. 2a*	0·5488	0·48764	0·75000	0·97861	No. 2a* ,, ,, ,, 0–5/16″
No. 3	0·8110	0·74610	1·21875	0·63898	No. 3 ,, ,, ,, 0–17/32″,
No. 4	1·1240	1·0372	1·6563	0·62886	1/8″–5/8″,
No. 5	1·4130	1·3161	1·8750	0·62010	3/16″–3/4″,
No. 6	0·0676	0·6241	1·0000	0·62292	1/4″–3/4″
					No. 4 ,, ,, ,, 1/8″–3/4″
					No. 5 ,, ,, ,, 3/8″–1″
					No. 6 ,, ,, ,, 0–1/2″

* For Short taper.

VIII. RECOMMENDED LUBRICANTS FOR MACHINING

Material	Turning	Drilling	Hand-reaming	Hand-tapping and Dieing	Milling
Aluminium	Paraffin or soluble oil	Paraffin; Tallow or beeswax (rubbed on drill)	Paraffin or soluble oil	Tallow or beeswax (rubbed on tool) or soluble oil	Paraffin, soapy water or dry
Brass	Dry or soluble oil	Dry or soluble oil	Soluble oil	Soluble oil	Dry or soluble oil
Bronze, Gunmetal	Dry	Dry or soluble oil	Soluble oil	Soluble oil	Dry or soluble oil
Cast Iron	Dry	Dry	Tallow and graphite (equal parts) rubbed on reamer	Dry or turpentine	Dry
Copper	Soluble oil or dry	Soluble oil or dry	Soluble oil and turpentine mixed	Dry or soluble oil	Dry or soluble oil
Duralumin	Paraffin, soluble oil or dry	Paraffin or soluble oil	Paraffin or soluble oil	Paraffin or soluble oil	Paraffin, soluble oil or dry
Ebonite	Soapy water	Dry	Inadvisable to ream	Dry	Dry or with paraffin or turpentine
Hard Fibre	Dry	Dry	Dry	Dry	Dry
Mild Steel	Soluble oil or soda water	Soluble oil or soda water	Soluble oil	Soluble oil	Soluble oil
Monel Metal	Soluble oil	Soluble oil	Soluble oil	Soluble oil	Soluble oil
Nickel Silver	Soluble oil	Soluble oil	Soluble oil	Soluble oil	Soluble oil
Phosphor Bronze	Soluble oil or dry	Soluble oil	Soluble oil	Soluble oil	Soluble oil
Silver Steel, Tool Steel	Soluble oil (twice normal strength)	Turpentine or soluble oil	Soluble oil	Soluble oil (twice normal strength)	Soluble oil
Stainless Steel	Coconut oil and turpentine or coconut oil and carbon tetrachloride	Soluble oil or turpentine	Soluble oil	Neatsfoot oil	Soluble oil
Wrought Iron	Soluble oil or soda water	Soluble oil or soda water	Soluble oil	Soluble oil	Soluble oil or soda water
Zinc-base Diecastings	Paraffin	Paraffin and soluble oil mixed	Paraffin and soluble oil mixed	Paraffin and soluble oil mixed	Paraffin and soluble oil mixed

In many cases lard oil would be considered a better lubricant than soluble oil, but in view of the expense and the difficulty of obtaining it, soluble oil has been substituted. Similarly, for small work and for average use the non-ferrous metals may be equally well machined dry, lubricants only being employed for production runs. In practically all cases, however, a little lubricant is recommended when reaming.

IX.   SURFACE SPEEDS FOR MACHINING METALS

These are offered only as a general guide, as the machining qualities of different metal samples vary widely. Speeds are also affected by the nature of the operation, the type of tool used, the rigidity of the machine itself and the state of bearings and slides. Much higher speeds are often used on high production machines.

As exactness in speed calculation is not usually called for, a rough calculation sufficiently accurate for practical purposes may be made as follows:

$$\frac{\text{Work dia. (ins.)} \quad \text{r.p.m.}}{4} = \text{surface speed in feet per minute}$$

	Feet per minute
Mild steel, normal quality	100–120
„ „ free cutting	120–150
Low carbon steel (Bessemer)	90–100
Medium carbon alloy or steel	80–90
High carbon steel (annealed)	70–80
Cast iron	60–70
Brass, free cutting	300–350
Yellow or cast brass	200–250
Bronze, medium hard	80–100
„ cast, hard	50–60
Copper	120
Cupro-nickel and nickel silver	100
Monel metal	80–100
Aluminium, soft alloys	300–350
„ hard alloys	120–150
„ wrought alloy (i.e. Duralumin)	100–120
Stainless steels (vary widely), free cutting	90–100
Plastics (also vary widely)	90–350

INDEX

BOOKS FOR THE MODEL ENGINEER

Building a Gauge 'O' Bassett-Lowke 2-6-0 Steam
 Locomotive
Building a 3½" Gauge Bassett-Lowke 0-6-0 Steam
 Locomotive
Building The Stuart Beam Engine
by Andrew Smith
Building the Stuart No 1 Engine
by Andrew Smith
The Clockmaker Volume 1
The Construction of a Bassett-Lowke 2½" Gauge
 4-6-2 'Flying Scotsman'
by J Camm
Dividing and Graduating
by George Thomas
Drummond's Lathe Work
Drummond 'M' Type Lathe
Drummond Round Bed Lathe
Early Lathes & Machine Tools of Interest
by C L Deith
Early Model Railway Locomotives of Interest
by C L Deith
Engineering in Miniature Bound Volumes
For Old Times Sake – 'Rainhill'
by LBSC
Gears for Small Mechanisms
by W O Davis
The Henley Anvil
The Henley Junior
How to Build a Traction Engine
by F J Camm
Instruction for the Working and General Manage-
 ment of Traction Engines and Steam Road Rollers
Instruction and Working Drawings for Building
 Small Steam Boilers
Introducing 'Bat' and 'Owl'
by LBSC
H Jubb & Son Ltd – Facsimile 1919 Catalogue
The Live Steam Book
by LBSC
Locomotive Valve Gears – A Practical Manual
 Maintenance and Management of Small
 Locomotives
by E H White
Making an Eight Day Longcase Clock
by Alan Timmins

Making a Skeleton Clock
by Paul N Hasluck
The Model Engineers Workshop Manual
by George Thomas
Model Stationary Engine
by H Muncaster
Myford Series 7 Lathe Manual
by Ian Bradley
Pattern Making
by F J Camm
The Quorn Universal Tool & Cutter Grinder
by Prof D H Chaddock
Small Dividing Head
Small Locomotive Construction – Introducing
 'Catapillar' a 4-12-4 Locomotive for 2½" Gauge
by LBSC
Small Locomotive Construction – How to Build
 'Eva May'
by LBSC
Small Locomotive Construction – How to Build a
 2½" Gauge 'Green Arrow'
by LBSC
Small Locomotive Construction – How to Build a
 Super High Speed Passenger Engine – 'Gwen
 Elms' a 2½" Gauge 4-6-4 Freelance Design
by LBSC
Small Locomotive Construction – How to Make a
 GWR Saddle Tank
by LBSC
Small Locomotive Construction – How to Build
 'Mabel Hall' a GWR 4-6-0 Locomotive for 2½"
 Gauge
by LBSC
Small Locomotive Construction – Building a Small
 Edition of the LMS Locomotive 'Princess Royal'
 for 2½" Gauge
by LBSC
Small Locomotive Construction – How to Build
 'Girton' a Schools Class Locomotive for Gauge 1
by LBSC
Stuart Turner Ltd Catalogue
Twin Cylinder Horizontal Engine
The 'Vulcan' Mill Engine
Wimshurst Machine
Workshop Masters Volume 1

 TEE Publishing

The Fosse, Fosse Way, Radford Semele, Leamington Spa, Warks. CV31 1XN
Telephone: 01926 614101   Fax: 01926 614293